*Small—On Safety*

Also available:

ACTION FOR A CHANGE: *A Student's Guide to Public Interest Organizing,* by Ralph Nader and Donald Ross

THE CHEMICAL FEAST: *Ralph Nader's Study Group Report on the Food and Drug Administration,* by James S. Turner

THE CLOSED ENTERPRISE SYSTEM: *Ralph Nader's Group Report on Antitrust Enforcement,* by Mark J. Green, with Beverly C. Moore, Jr., and Bruce Wasserstein

THE COMPANY STATE: *Ralph Nader's Study Group Report on Dupont in Delaware,* by James Phelan and Robert Pozen

THE INTERSTATE COMMERCE OMISSION: *Ralph Nader's Study Group on the Interstate Commerce Commission and Transportation,* by Robert C. Fellmeth

OLD AGE: THE LAST SEGREGATION: *Ralph Nader's Study Group Report on Nursing Homes,* Claire Townsend, Project Director

POLITICS OF LAND: *Ralph Nader's Study Group Report on Land Use in California,* Robert C. Fellmeth, Project Director

SOWING THE WIND: *A Report for Ralph Nader's Center for Study of Responsive Law on Food Safety and the Chemical Harvest,* by Harrison Wellford

UNSAFE AT ANY SPEED: *The Designed-in Danger of the American Automobile* (expanded and updated, 1972), by Ralph Nader

VANISHING AIR: *Ralph Nader's Study Group Report on Air Pollution,* by John C. Esposito

THE WATER LORDS: *Ralph Nader's Study Group Report on Industry and Environmental Crisis in Savannah, Georgia,* by James M. Fallows

WATER WASTELAND: *Ralph Nader's Study Group Report on Water Pollution,* by David Zwick and Marcy Benstock

WHAT TO DO WITH YOUR BAD CAR: *An Action Manual for Lemon Owners,* by Ralph Nader, Lowell Dodge, and Ralf Hotchkiss

WHISTLE BLOWING: *The Report of the Conference on Professional Responsibility,* edited by Ralph Nader, Peter J. Petkas, and Kate Blackwell

THE WORKERS: *Portraits of Nine American Jobholders,* by Kenneth Lasson

*The Center for Auto Safety*
Project Editors: Lowell Dodge, Ralf Hotchkiss,
Carl Nash, Stephen Oesch, and Bernard O'Meara

# Small–On Safety

## *The Designed-in Dangers of the Volkswagen*

Grossman Publishers New York 1972

Published in 1972 by Grossman Publishers
625 Madison Avenue, New York, N.Y. 10022
Published simultaneously in Canada by
Fitzhenry and Whiteside, Ltd.
SBN 670-65249-0
Library of Congress Catalogue Card Number: 70-184477
Printed in U.S.A.

The royalties from the sale of this book will go to further the work of the Center for Auto Safety on safety hazards resulting from poor design or assembly of cars, consumer problems of the auto industry, and related areas. Contributions to the Center for Auto Safety are tax deductible and should be sent to P.O. Box 7250, Ben Franklin Station, Washington, D.C. 20004.

# *Project Contributors*

Clarence Ditlow
- B.S., Chemical Engineering, Lehigh University
- J.D., Georgetown University Law Center
- LL.M., Harvard Law School

Lowell Dodge
- B.A., Yale University
- J.D., Harvard Law School

Ralf Hotchkiss
- B.A., Physics, Oberlin College

Justin Klein
- B.A., University of Pennsylvania
- 3rd year law student, National Law Center, George Washington University

Jason Mirabito
- B.S., Physics, New York University
- 1st year law student, American University Law School

Carl Nash
- Ph.D., Physics, University of North Carolina, Chapel Hill

Stephen Oesch
- B.A., The College of Wooster, Wooster, Ohio
- 1st year law student, Georgetown University Law Center

Bernard O'Meara
- B.S., Engineering and Applied Sciences, Yale University

Kenneth Simons
- 1st year undergraduate, Yale University

Danny Snyder
- B.I.D., Syracuse University
- graduate student, Syracuse University

Gregory Williams
- 5th year honors student, engineering, Massachusetts Institute of Technology

## *Production Assistants*

Claire Cannon
Arthur Delibert
Mike Gregoire
Klaus Heimburg
Karen ter Horst
Eileen Kane
Vinson Kelley
Jane Kniffin
Doris Lasley
Diane Lattin
Susan Perry
Connie Jo Smith
Adele Winters

*To the memory of*
*Michael and Betty Wollan*

# Contents

# *Introduction by Ralph Nader*

A gentleman from St. Louis recently added to our VW complaint file a letter which began this way:

> A recent advertisement for Volkswagens caused me to give a good deal of thought to something that has been troubling me for some time. First of all, several years ago a friend's daughter was killed when her VW was overturned by the wind and ran off the road. It was thought of at that time as a freakish accident and not until I learned of an accident within a mile of my office about a month or so ago when another friend's son was killed when his VW was virtually "blown off" a local highway, into a concrete pillar, did I feel these were more than freakish occurrences.

Five years earlier, a specialist in vehicle dynamics, Professor E. E. Larrabee of M.I.T., gave experimental support to the folklore that "some truck drivers hesitate to pass Volkswagens on narrow roads at high speeds for fear of disturbing the car to the extent that the driver may lose control."

These are not the images which Volkswagen tries to convey in the uniquely self-effacing immodesty that characterizes its advertisements. By playing the ugly underdog theme, it touts its engineering, durability, quality, and economy. "Of course, it took great fortitude to resist squandering our time on phony styling improvements," said one ad. "The Beetle looks just as good (or bad) as it did 25 years ago." Or as another ad put it: "First off, there's no doubt about it, the only way to make an economy car is expensively. So Rule No. 1, don't scrimp."

This study group report documents a major form of Volkswagenwerk A. G. scrimping—on safety! The Volkswagen is the most hazardous vehicle used in significant numbers in the United States. Ironically the domestic auto makers must take much of the blame for this fact. Had they not failed, in their lumbering fashion, to recognize and meet a sizable market for an easier-to-park, more economical, and relatively simple vehicle, the VW Beetles would not have swarmed into this country like a plague of locusts. Motorists might have been spared so many seriously unstable Beetles, which in a crash have collapse characteristics reminiscent of a Japanese lantern.

Volkswagen took relentless advantage of Detroit's gas-guzzling behemoths and directed its marketing strategy toward the economizers and the intellectuals. By showing motorists an alternative to Detroit, VW enticed them into the maw of Wolfsburg. The company's promotions literally boasted for many years that readers couldn't tell one year's VW from another as if to transform its technological stagnation into a virtue. And it's not for lack of money that VW has stagnated.*

Over the years, the attitude of VW's top management has been just the opposite of the surface candor which exudes from the advertisements. Secrecy has long been a company trademark and, accompanied by not a little

* The company has more than conventional mark-up margins available for engineering safety improvements. Pound for dollar a new VW Beetle is more expensive than new mass-market American cars. In addition, notwithstanding its apparent simplicity in design, the cost per pound of four automobile replacement body parts (hood, right front fender, right front door, right rear quarter panel) for the 1971 Beetle totaled $2.35 per pound, compared with $2.11 per pound for the Chevrolet Impala, $1.91 for the Opel Kadett, $1.98 for the Ford Capri, $2.16 for the Plymouth Fury, and $1.59 for the Chevrolet Vega. Although the study by the Insurance Institute for Highway Safety included higher figures for some models other than the Beetle, the results hardly support VW's self-styled reputation for this kind of economy. The total weight of the Beetle's four replacement parts is the lowest in this study, a hint of the VW's abysmal crush characteristics. What may be an economy in a minor collision may lead to a staggering loss in a more serious crash.

smugness, a kind of corporate subculture. This is, of course, a tragic devolution of corporate character which has redounded again and again against the flowering of engineering-safety genius within the company. The lack of a consumer movement in Germany and the absence of a critical engineering tradition with access to governmental authority led to an overwhelming dominance of the corporation over the state in safety matters. With the reasoning of a mad logician, VW persuades its public that an unchanging car is economical and a car is economical because it's unchanging. In recent years, this tight ball of yarn has begun to unravel—faster and faster. There is increasing awareness outside the auto industry that many significant engineering safety changes now being adopted by various manufacturers use the same or cost-comparable materials and labor that went into making their less safe predecessors. In addition, VW began telling people a tale not of its wanting—namely, that the Beetle could change but only if required to do so by government safety standards. Two years ago, in a frank comment, D. Friedrich Goes, chief of auto safety research for VW, told automotive reporter Bob Irvin of the Detroit *News:* "Government regulations are just another type of technical battle. If they want a padded dash they get it. If they want a side guard rail, it's no problem to put one in."

This position indicates that the company will wait until sufficient external pressure is applied before it takes its safety features and technical skills off the shelf. But Dr. Goes's comment does not reveal the extent to which VW is prepared to oppose and defeat proposed government safety standards. Toward this objective VW has far more leverage than its 4½ percent of the vehicles on U.S. highways would normally provide. As the world's third largest auto manufacturer and largest vehicle exporter, VWAG registered sales of $4.2 billion last year and sold a total of 2,211,000 vehicles. As the oldest established importer into the U.S. market, with the largest dealer network, VW also receives support in its lobbying activities from other foreign auto companies which sell to America. Because General Motors and Ford have plants in West Germany with very substantial sales,* those two companies are anxious not to antagonize VW by pushing for the kind of safety standards they know that they, but not VW, can quickly meet. The prospects of economic retaliation are too obvious.

For these and other reasons of international economics and politics, the State Department wasted no time in late 1966 and 1967 intervening before the National Highway Traffic Safety Administration (NHTSA) on behalf of foreign cars. The critical question the State Department and the foreign imports wanted answered was whether NHTSA was going to require the highest level of auto safety then available on the market and off the shelf or whether the standards would cater to the lowest common denominators so fulsomely reflected in the VW Beetle. The answer was not long in coming. No standards would be issued which would disturb the Beetle level of hazard in any fundamental way. The changes were limited either to attachable devices, such as seat belts and shoulder harnesses, or to simply-installable components, such as an energy-absorbing steering assembly.

The basic and lasting defects in the VW Beetle and microbus design discussed in this report remain unperturbed by the federal standards. These include woefully inadequate front and side crashworthiness, handling instability, poor seat design, and other hazards which are easily correctable even from the standpoint of available or applied engineering practice.

VW's little publicized victory (all the attention was on Detroit) over the federal government's safety program provided the company with a range of facile defenses to safety criticism. These defenses are based on claims of meeting all applicable federal safety standards. First, as the report shows, VW has failed a large proportion of compliance tests conducted by the government. Second, the standards fail to cover major safety areas, such as handling capability. Third, the standards

* In 1971 Ford Motor Company sold 767,128 cars and trucks which Ford manufactured in Germany. (From Ford Annual Report 1971.)

In 1971 General Motors Corporation sold 824,354 cars and trucks which GM manufactured in Germany. (From General Motors Annual Report 1971.)

are very weak, in significant measure because VW and its industry associates wanted them that way. Fourth, there has been a near standstill in the issuance of important safety standards since 1968 for application to 1969, 1970, 1971, and 1972 models.

Not content with such government timidity in issuing meaningful standards, VW exerts strenuous pressure to prevent government crash testing of VWs and disclosure of the results publicly. The former head of the NHTSA, Dr. William Haddon, was so disturbed by the unique hazards of the VW Beetle that he ordered a series of crash tests on the car. After Haddon revealed, on the day of his departure to make way for the incoming Nixon administration, that the first VW crash tests were completed, VW charged that it was being singled out for unfair treatment and insinuated that such tests were inspired by its domestic competitors. In fact the VW tests signaled the commencement of a larger program to develop a vehicle-crash survivability index for consumers to compare the safety of vehicles by make and model. But as a result of the VW uproar, the new management at the Department of Transportation refused to show the crash-test films to the public until forced to do so two months later by Senator Vance Hartke at his Senate Commerce subcommittee hearing. And the program was shelved by the Department in cooperation with the White House Office of Management and Budget despite promises to the contrary under the spotlight of congressional hearings.

The other aspect of VW's response pattern to criticism is the trotting out of alleged "research findings" by "independent testing firms" which happen to be funded by Volkswagen. Even when one of the company's better known contractors, the Cornell Aeronautical Laboratory, places the best possible verbal impression on its dubiously categorized data, VW then circulates secret memos to its dealers with additional reinterpreted distortions of the Cornell information. It also provides its dealers and other inquirers with standard obfuscations of other studies and to support its safety claims compares its Beetle with other small imported cars, even though they are sold in far less significant numbers.

The company could provide the public with a simple test series. Would VW place an unbelted test driver in a conventional 1964 VW Beetle and crash it into a fixed barrier at a mere 15 mph? And would VW place a belted test driver in a conventional 1971 VW Beetle and crash it into a fixed barrier at a mere 30 mph? And would the company conduct such tests in public with the results and test procedures available to specialists for checking? The company's reluctance to do so might be understandable from the standpoint of occupational safety practices. Conducting the same tests with the VW microbus would be out of the question for anything but anthropomorphic dummies. But if VW could safely conduct the former tests, it might begin a process of long overdue credibility that the car maker very much needs.

The following report, produced by specialists in physics, engineering, and law, strives to enlarge upon a young tradition of informed consumer criticism of automotive-engineering design. It is clear, and implicitly admitted by VW officials, that the company's recent allocation of greater funding and technical resources to its auto safety research is due to governmental and public pressure mostly from the United States. The company is now working on a special "safety car," which one hopes will become part of its future marketing plans for this country. Should the NHTSA be permitted by higher politically appointed governmental officials to issue the significant standards which have been held back for so long, the VW Beetle will in effect be precluded from entry into the American market without drastic engineering changes or replacement with a new VW model entirely. Certainly, American officials who have seen the early work of the crack engineering-safety research team being assembled in Wolfsburg have been impressed by the life-saving potential of such liberated engineering talent. VW has the resources to produce a safe car and, as the first and biggest exporter to the United States, its initiatory responsibility to do so is paramount. The question is whether company management will give its engineers and scientists the opportunity to do so.

But one must look back as well as forward. Even if the sale of Beetles were immediately stopped, millions of the dangerous cars would remain on the highways. Something must be done about them. Beginning after the passage of the 1966 United States auto safety law, a new ethic has gradually been imposed on auto manufacturers, making them responsible at least for acknowledging past or present vehicle defects. (The law presently requires defect notification, but paradoxically not defect correction.) Clearly, if a company sells defective merchandise to unsuspecting consumers, it should be required at least to correct such products, if not to compensate for the casualties and property damage due to defective design.

This report details the need for Volkswagen to observe that ethical imperative and recall all the Beetles for safety modifications. The net cost, calculated in Chapter 7, is not at all out of range, given the size of the company's sales and profits and the lifesaving and injury-avoiding potential of such a move. A recall of Beetles would also become an effective deterrent against future defects and a weighty support for those safety-design engineers inside the company who are urging faster improvements.

Volkswagen has already spent a fortune in public relations and other expenses to cover up or to repress the engineering truth about its vehicles. Unless it starts responding with action, not words, it will have to spend a great deal more. There are rumblings within the company of late which indicate that the days of monolithic policies without dissents or without outside appeals are past.

A humane, farsighted policy is open to VW management. With a solid emphasis on engineering innovation —a priority attainable by drawing on more of its untapped science-engineering talent—the company can avoid the industry tradition of defiance and intransigence based on the belief that enough influence and money will block the imposition of stronger standards and judicial sanctions. It is not entirely a secret that VW lawyers and top officials are viewing with the utmost concern the large increase in lawsuits filed by injured plaintiffs in U.S. courts over the past two years. Mass recalls will diminish the spread of such litigation and, more importantly, the spread of casualties incurred through defects which could have been avoided at such little cost by means of simple engineering practices. It is particularly this fact—that the main deficiencies which make the Beetle so distinctly hazardous were violations of known and inexpensive engineering-safety standards—that requires such corporate redemption.

Looking ahead, if what Volkswagen is waiting for is further pressure from external stimuli, the present course of events will not inevitably disappoint the company. This report, with its gathering of facts and analyses about the VW's hazards, should provide a useful information service for any safety-minded constituency advocating humane engineering of motor vehicles. It is likely, as a result, to lead to the production of more information about Volkswagens and company practices—both desirable and undesirable—and to future studies from the consumer-motorist perspective.

At a time when earthshaking problems are making far greater demands for change by entrenched interests and powers, the crime and tragedy of trivial neglects, like those infecting the Beetle and microbus, is their ability to cause such profound human devastation. Against the excessive toll of life, limb, and property, can any executive of the companies look deep into his conscience and say that whatever was gained was worth that much to Volkswagenwerk AG, of Wolfsburg, West Germany, and Volkswagen of America, Inc., of Englewood Cliffs, New Jersey?

# *Foreword*

The Beetle has swept America. While only one VW was imported into the United States in 1949, 1970 sales totaled 569,182 for all types of VWs. This is 7 percent of all automobiles and 46 percent of all foreign cars sold in the United States in 1970. VW has overtaken all but Ford, Chevrolet, Plymouth, Pontiac, and Buick in annual U.S. sales.[1] There are about 3.9 million VWs of all types in America today, the vast majority of which are Beetles.[2]

The Beetle's history dates from 1930.[3] Late that year a German auto designer, Ferdinand Porsche, created a design for a small car known then only as "Project 12." The design incorporated many of the distinctive characteristics of the later Volkswagen, including an air-cooled, horizontally opposed, four-cylinder engine located behind the rear axle, and a torsion-bar rear swing axle suspension with trailing links. The prototype "Project 12" was completed in 1932. Tests revealed problems, however, and plans to mass-produce the car were abandoned when Porsche's financial backers lost interest.

After another false start, Porsche found a backer with virtually unlimited resources—Adolph Hitler. Hitler, then on his rise to power, saw the idea of a low-priced "people's car" as a means of winning and holding the support of the German working population. Prototypes were completed in 1937 and tested in 1938. In

May, 1938, construction began on a plant in Wolfsburg which would be capable of turning out 400,000 Volkswagens per year. After only 2500 cars had been made, production was interrupted by the war.

About 10,000 VWs were produced in 1946 at Wolfsburg, after war damage to the factory had been sufficiently repaired. A resolute, assertive engineer, Heinz Nordhoff, brought annual production of the VW from 19,000 in 1948 (his first year as chief executive) to more than 1,700,000 in 1968 (his last year with the company).[4]

In 1949, Volkswagen's first attempt to export Beetles to the U.S. was aborted. The next year, a New York auto dealer specializing in imports took on VWs as a sideline and sold 330 of them. Between 1953 and 1958, the VW organization in the United States was consolidated by a German businessman, Will Van de Camp. In 1956, Volkswagen of America (VWoA) was established at Englewood Cliffs, N.J., as the factory-owned, sole importer of VWs.[5] Over 55,000 VWs were imported into the U.S. that year.

VWoA's system of regional distributors, each of which selects and franchises dealerships in its area, took shape under Carl Hahn, another German, who headed VWoA from 1959 to 1964. Hahn's policies included emphasis on service, uniform building plans for dealerships, required stocking of parts, and purchasing recommendations for each dealer, which even included the desks and the lamps on them.

In some respects the message of the Beetle has been a positive one, and the cleverly conceived advertising for VW has consistently pressed this point home. The Volkswagen features relative economy of operation and repair, ease in parking, and no major annual styling changes. The Beetle, leading other imports, has goaded American automakers into curtailing some of their more flamboyant excesses, and has probably helped keep domestic car prices down. On the other hand, the VW warranty has in the past been of shorter duration than that of domestic makes.[6] Reliable and efficient repairs are much more difficult to obtain than VW ads would have us believe, and there exist VW "lemons" just as there are lemons of other makes.[7]

And most important, Volkswagen remains virtually silent about its most serious problem—vehicle safety. Neither the likelihood of a Beetle becoming involved in a crash nor the safety of its occupants during a crash have been adequately discussed. VWoA's safety pronouncements have been directed largely at glossing over the safety problems of the Beetle for the benefit of VW dealers and salesmen. A 1968 safety report by VWoA on the Beetle addressed to dealers states: "We believe that . . . our car is the safest small car in the world." [8] We know of no sources outside or inside VW which could have provided the basis for such an ambitious appraisal. In fact, until 1966, Volkswagen had no office, section, or department which could be identified as having safety as its primary mission or concern.[9]

This report, therefore, assesses the safety of the VW. It focuses primarily on the Type I (popularly known as the Beetle or Bug),[10] but also includes a brief section on the Type II (the microbus). The report is based on publicly available research reports, on the records of court cases brought against Volkswagen,[11] and on individual case studies from many sources which are now part of the files of the Center for Auto Safety.

The conclusion drawn in this report is that the Beetle has many serious design defects which have been responsible for the deaths and injuries of thousands of people. These are deaths which could have been prevented and injuries which could at least have been reduced in severity had Volkswagen been as aggressive in its safety policies as in its marketing. The report finally concludes that it is the responsibility of Volkswagen to correct these defects through design improvements in future VWs and a recall campaign for those already produced so that further avoidable deaths and injuries will not occur.

We should explain why we have singled out VW. There are several reasons. Since there are large numbers of VWs on American roads, their design defects are affecting many people. Partly as a result of VW's success there has been sufficient study of it to expose most of its safety problems, while similar defects have not been analyzed in less common cars. Moreover, because the VW is the leader of the subcompact field, it is almost solely responsible for both the wave of domestic compact cars around 1960 and the new series of sub-compact United States-made cars. An unfortunate example of emulation of the Beetle occurred in 1960 when the Corvair copied some of its worst features.[12] As the leader in its rapidly growing field, VW must assume an extra measure of responsibility for safe design. Most of all, however, we have singled out the Volkswagen simply because it is the most dangerous car sold in significant numbers in the United States today.

## *Small—On Safety*

# 1

## *Crashworthiness and Passenger Safety*

Many people had long suspected that small cars are less safe in a crash than large cars; their fears were confirmed in late 1964 when Cornell Aeronautical Laboratory's Automobile Crash Injury Research (ACIR) Project released its study of crash injury as a function of car size.[1] Five years later, the New York State Department of Motor Vehicles found that for crashes occurring in that state, the likelihood of serious or fatal injury goes up exponentially as the weight of the car decreases (Figure 1).[2]

The ACIR study was particularly disturbing to Volkswagen since nearly half of the small cars in the sample area were VWs. Volkswagen feared that publicity given to this study would adversely affect sales at a time when they were consolidating their capture of close to 5 percent of the American market. So, apparently to counter the bad publicity from the report, Volkswagen commissioned a study to be carried out by ACIR dealing specifically with the VW Beetle.[3] The data in the original ACIR study are based on a sample of 27,552 crash-involved vehicles, of which 879 were VW Beetles, 325 were Renaults, and 391 were other foreign makes. The sample contains data from crashes in which at least one person was injured occurring in rural areas of 30 states. The vehicles are primarily pre-1966 models and are all two- or four-door sedans.

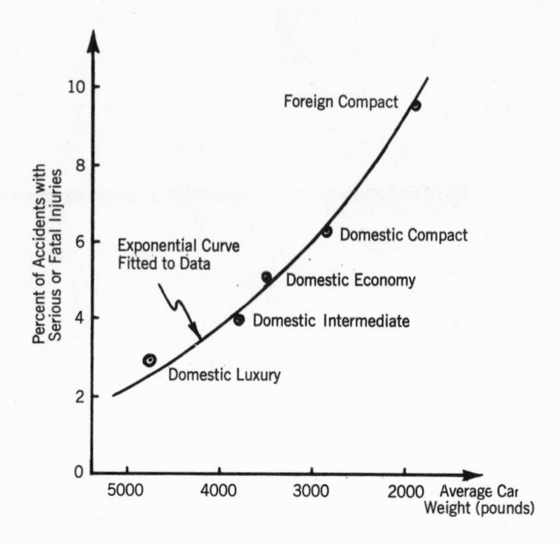


*Figure 1.* Percent of crash-involved vehicles in which the most serious injury was fatal or serious. Source: New York State Department of Motor Vehicles study conducted for the National Highway Traffic Safety Administration.

In this study, overall injury statistics for occupants of vehicles involved in injury-producing crashes were as follows: [4]

| *Car Group* | *% of Occupants with Dangerous or Fatal Injuries* | *% of Fatalities among Occupants* |
|---|---|---|
| Volkswagen | 13.1 | 5.0 |
| Renault | 11.4 | 4.6 |
| Other Foreign Sedans | 9.4 | 4.8 |
| Corvair | 10.1 | 5.5 |
| Pre-1956 U.S. Sedans | | |
| Light | 10.2 | 3.2 |
| Intermediate I | 9.5 | 4.2 |
| Standard | 9.0 | 3.5 |
| Intermediate II | 9.8 | 4.9 |
| Heavy | 9.9 | 4.7 |
| Post-1955 U.S. Sedans | | |
| Light | 10.5 | 4.6 |
| Intermediate I | 10.1 | 4.6 |
| Standard | 8.8 | 3.7 |
| Intermediate II | 9.2 | 4.4 |
| Heavy | 9.9 | 4.3 |

When ACIR personnel studied these crashes, they found that the most common type for the VW was the "principal rollover." [5] This is defined as a crash in which major damage to the car is associated with a rollover, although both collision and rollover may have taken place. Of the Volkswagen crashes, 40.6 percent were principal rollovers; by comparison, for other foreign sedans (except Renault [6]), 30.2 percent of crashes were principal rollovers. The VW figures are alarming, not only because of the frequency of principal rollovers, but also because *69 percent of these rollovers occurred in the absence of collision,* indicating serious instability in the car.

ACIR further computed the speed above which the chance of rollover in a collision is greater than 50 percent. For the Beetle, this speed is 50 mph, while for other foreign sedans (except Renault), this speed is 62 mph. By contrast, American cars in the study had a less than 50 percent chance of rollover in crashes at speeds up to 80 mph.[7]

The rollover problem is but one of the Volkswagen's distinctive hazards. The ACIR study found that pre-1966 Beetles displayed other safety-related problems: (1) Occupants of Beetles were ejected from their vehicles much more frequently than from virtually any other contemporary vehicle. Drivers of VWs were ejected in 11 percent of all collisions and in 36 percent of all rollovers. Corresponding figures for other foreign cars (except Renault) were 9.5 percent and 27.4 percent, while for light American cars the figures are 5.7 percent and 20 percent.[8]

The propensity of Beetles to eject their occupants is a particularly important deficiency since, as the report states,[9]

> . . . more than 90 percent of those ejected [from all cars in the study] were injured, compared with approximately 70 to 80 percent for non-ejected occupants. The percentage of dangerous and fatal, or fatal injuries, among ejectees generally was three to six times greater than among non-ejectees.

Concerning the Beetle itself, they commented, "The use of seat belts and a properly designed safety door latch to reduce door opening should reduce occupant ejection and consequently, injury severity."[10] (The dangers resulting from the design of VW door-latch assemblies will be examined in Chapter 3.)

(2) When a VW is hit from the front, the odds are greater than one in four (the exact figure is 26.1 percent) that the seat tracks, which hold the seat in place, will be damaged. This figure is only a little higher than for other cars; what is important is that in 38.8 percent of these cases, the seat was torn completely loose from its track. When this happens in a rear impact, the occupant and his seat can be thrown into the rear of the car, injuring him and the rear passengers. The seat's occupant can even be ejected out the rear window, since the seat belt and shoulder harness offer little or no restraint to such rearward movement. Seat-track damage occurred in 22 percent of all VW collisions, and it was most common when the car was hit from behind.[11] (The "VW ejector seat" is described more fully in Chapter 3.)

(3) Steering-column penetration into the passenger compartment occurred in 16.9 percent of the crashed Beetles, topped only by the Corvair with 21.3 percent penetration.[12] These cars share a design defect: the steering box (located at the forward end of the steering column) is ahead of the front axle. Thus, in a front-end collision, the first solid part of the car that the colliding object meets after the bumper is the steering box, which in turn pushes the steering column and wheel backward into the driver's chest.

(4) The Beetle was found to be more vulnerable to side impacts than other cars. Only 81 percent of the Beetles were left with their interior compartments intact after side impact, compared to almost 90 percent for most other cars.[13]

(5) The top structure of the Beetle was found to cause 4.5 percent of the major injuries to occupants, compared to 2.7 percent for other foreign cars, and around 2 percent for most domestic cars.[14] This figure can only partly be explained by the propensity of the VW to roll over; the weakness of the car's roof is also an important factor.

In spite of these figures, however, ACIR concluded that "Overall, the structural integrity of the Volkswagen compartment area appears to be maintained as well as that in any other car."[15] The study cites passenger ejection as the most serious safety problem with the Beetle.[16] If ACIR's assessment is correct, it would follow that VW could make improvements in the Beetle's safety by insuring that occupants stay in the car and are held in place during a crash by installing adequate door-latch assemblies and an effective occupant-restraint system. But ejection is only one of the problems.

The ACIR study emphatically stresses that the safety problems of pre-1966 Beetles are not due primarily to their small size. In at least one important respect, ACIR is wrong. According to ACIR's own data, the major cause of actual injury to occupants of Beetles is the windshield. It causes 20.5 percent of all occupant injuries, the highest for any vehicle in the study.[17] By comparison, ejection from Beetles was responsible for 11.8 percent of Beetle-occupant injuries. Because of the Beetle's small size, there is little space between the occupant and the windshield—a factor in the high proportion of windshield injuries that is still a serious problem even if present lap and shoulder belts are used. The windshield is so close that loosely belted occupants can impact it.

The size and configuration of the VW contribute significantly to crash injuries. In shorter cars, the gas tank is necessarily closer to the occupants than in larger cars. The propensity of the VW to roll over results in part from its configuration. The Beetle's center of gravity is much higher in relation to the car's track-width than almost every American car's; the result is an unstable vehicle.

Yet another hazardous result of the Beetle's small size is the lack of effective collapse distance, which is necessary to absorb some of the forces generated by a crash. A shorter car must compromise collapse distance for interior space, or vice versa. The VW compromises both. The lack of interior space is evidenced by the windshield injuries cited above. The inadequate crush distance results from the design of the Beetle's front and rear structures. A recent report by the British Road Research Laboratory criticized the design of the front. It states: "The front of the car was relatively easily deformed [in crash tests] for the first 46 cm (18 in.), at which point the 'backbone' chassis member was reached when the car behaved in a very rigid manner.

This characteristic gave rise to high seat belt loads and high relative impact velocities for unrestrained dummies." [18] The already short crush distance is further—and unnecessarily—diminished by the location of the steering box, which is in front of the front axle. After the front has been crushed about a foot, the end of the rigid steering column is contacted and the column is pushed rearward into the driver.* And, as the British study noted, after only six more inches the head of the chassis itself is reached.

The lack of rear crush distance and the stiffness of the rear of the car is evidenced by the incidence of seat failure in rear-end collisions, which is discussed in more detail in Chapter 3. The rear bumper, engine lid, and muffler of the VW offer little energy absorption. Thus the force of a collision is rapidly transmitted to the engine and the chassis, resulting in a severe jolt.

Lateral crush distance is extremely small in all VWs due to their narrow width. Data show the Beetle to be more vulnerable to severe penetration or crushing of the occupant space than any car in wide use except the Corvair.[19]

The lack of collapse distance in the doors results in part from VW's attempts to maximize the effective passenger compartment width while minimizing cost.

There are other dangers with smaller cars which result from their lower weight. A light car should be as safe as any other in a collision with a fixed barrier, if the crashworthiness is equal in both. However, given the same crashworthiness, a lighter car will fare much worse than a heavier car in a collision between the two. If all cars were Beetle-sized and adequately crashworthy, fatalities and injuries to the occupants of the smaller cars could conceivably be eliminated. But Volkswagen collisions with other automobiles account for slightly more than half of all VW collisions.[20] They also collide with trucks, buses, other vehicles, roadside obstacles, and

* A telescoping, energy absorbing steering column should catch the driver in a crash and decrease his injuries, *if* the steering wheel is oriented so that the driver's chest hits the steering wheel over a large surface area. The 1968 model and newer Beetles have collapsible steering columns which will compress approximately six inches and thus absorb part of the energy of the crash. Since, however, the steering column extends in front of the front axle, it can still be thrust back into the driver's chest after this deformation has taken place.

suffer damage in rollovers which do not involve collision.

Volkswagen of America paid $30,000 for the ACIR study of its cars; the findings do not particularly favor the Beetle. As the Head of Research at the Cornell Laboratory said in a letter to U.S. Senator Warren Magnuson [21] ". . . our report's recommendations for the safety improvements of the Volkswagen automobile are quite specific and contain few, if any, 'accolades.' " He added, "As you can readily determine by reading our final report, it is hardly laudatory of Volkswagen." In reporting the results of this study to its dealers, VWoA nevertheless stated, "As this published study demonstrates, we are making every effort to give our vehicle outstanding crashworthiness as well as dependability and economy . . . We believe that this study . . . demonstrates that our car is the safest small car in the world." [22] VWoA has commissioned a second study, to include 1966 and later models, to be released shortly.

A second study by Dr. B. J. Campbell, formerly of ACIR, is a statistical analysis of information on 270,697 vehicles involved in crashes in North Carolina in 1966 and 1968.[23] For the sample as a whole, 84 percent of the drivers were not injured, while 7.4 percent received serious injury (defined as a bleeding wound, a distorted member, or any condition that incapacitates the driver), and 0.5 percent were killed.

By taking into account car speed, site of impact on the car, type of accident, type of injury to the driver, and the year, make, and body style of the car, Dr. Campbell was able to devise an injury-severity index. The number 100 was chosen as the index for the standard rate of injury. Individual makes were assigned a number on this scale such that the higher the index number, the greater the likelihood that the driver would sustain serious or fatal injuries. An index number was assigned to any make which was represented at least 100 times in the total sample. Standards of statistical analysis were applied to determine whether the assignment was significantly different from the average for all cars.

The range of serious and fatal injury index numbers ran from a high of over 200 for the VW microbus to a low of under 50 for several late-model General Motors full-size cars. Numbers were assigned both for total injuries and for the sum of serious and fatal injuries. The relevant data for other small cars are as follows:[24]

DRIVER INJURY

| *Make (year model)* | *Number in Sample* | *Index Number All Injuries* | *Index Number Serious and Fatal* |
|---|---|---|---|
| VW microbus (all years)* | 195 | 170 | 200+ |
| MG (all years) | 419 | 158 | 200 |
| Renault (all years) | 384 | 185 | 145 |
| Corvair (1960–63) | 1583 | 139 | 150 |
| VW Beetle (1960–67) | 3941 | 141 | 143 |
| Valiant (1960–66) | 1516 | 134 | 139 |
| VW Beetle (1968) | 331 | 136 | N.S.** |
| VW Type III (all years) | 250 | 134 | N.S. |
| Corvair (1964) | 377 | 134 | N.S. |
| Chevy II (1962–67) | 2108 | 119 | 125 |
| Falcon (1960–65) | 3748 | 124 | 124 |

* The VW microbus was the only van-type vehicle included in the Campbell study. However, since it usually carries a higher than average number of passengers, its inclusion seems warranted in a study of passenger vehicles.

** N.S. denotes not statistically significant (see note 24).

In his testimony before Congress, Dr. Campbell said:

> It should be of more than passing interest to drivers to know that in the event of a crash their chance of a serious or fatal injury is associated with the car they are driving, and that depending on their choice, the "odds" could be reduced 50 percent or increased 100 percent.[25]

Since all types of VWs represented less than 2 percent of the total sample, it is not likely that VW was over-represented in the total accident statistics. However, from the Campbell data it can be estimated that, in the event of a crash, the VW Beetle is between 1.5 and 3 times more likely to produce serious injury or death than a late-model, full-size sedan.*

* Dr. Campbell has recently completed an updating of his 1970 study of Driver Injury in Automobile Accidents with a greatly increased data base. Although his results had not been published as of April 14, 1972, when they were requested, Dr. Campbell graciously made them available to all interested parties in advance of their formal release. For the Volkswagen, as for most cars, the updated

In a third study, crashes occurring in New York during the first nine months of 1968 were reported by the New York State Department of Motor Vehicles.[26] Of these, 15,573 were Volkswagens. The following is a list of eight sedans of similar size and one station wagon, along with the percentage of vehicles which were involved in serious crashes, the percentage of drivers who sustained serious or fatal injuries, and the percentage of cars in noncollision accidents:

| *Make* | *% Vehicles* * | *% Drivers Injured* | *% Cars in Non-Collision Accidents* |
|---|---|---|---|
| Datsun | 9.3– 8.9 | 7.1 | 3.6 |
| Fiat | 8.4– 8.4 | 6.4 | 3.4 |
| Opel | 8.7– 8.0 | 6.7 | 3.9 |
| Renault | 10.5–10.6 | 9.7 | 6.3 |
| Saab | 8.2– 7.6 | 6.5 | 5.3 |
| Simca | 7.0– — | 5.6 | — |
| Toyota | 4.2– — | 2.5 | — |
| Volkswagen | 10.2–10.2 | 8.2 | 6.0 |
| Volkswagen Sta. Wgn. | — –10.4 | — | 9.2 |

* The first column of vehicle percentages comes from the *Interim Report,* the second, updated, from the *Hearings* (see note 26), % Drivers was given in *Interim Report,* % Cars in Non-Collision Accidents in *Hearings.*

---

figures generally reinforced the original findings of the 1970 study. The results are as follows (figures shown in brackets are from original study):

| *Make (year model)* | *Number in Sample* | *Index Number All Injuries* | *Index Number Serious and Fatal* |
|---|---|---|---|
| VW Beetle (1960–67) | 7910 | 139 | 144 |
| | [3864] | [141] | [143] |
| VW Beetle (1968–70) | 2692 | 136 | 135 |
| | [331] | [136] | [128*] |
| VW Microbus (all years) | 564 | 140 | 163 |
| | [176] | [170] | [200+] |
| VW Type III (all years) | 1065 | 128 | 115* |
| | [250] | [134] | [132*] |

* These figures are not significant. All other figures in the table have significance at the .01 level (highly significant).

An interesting sidelight from the updated Campbell study is a comparison of accident type for the pre-1968 and post-1967 Beetles. For the earlier Beetles (which had a swing axle rear suspension), "car ran off road" (presumably most of the single-vehicle accidents) accounted for 23.08% of all accidents. The later VWs (most of which had double-jointed rear axles) showed some improvement in this category as the figure dropped to 18.35%. This is slightly higher than the average percentage for all cars in the study, 16.62% of which "ran off road."

Even though the VW appears to be involved in crashes no more often than would be expected from their total numbers in the state of New York, *more* than the expected percentage of drivers were injured in Volkswagen accidents. Several English sports cars fared as poorly as did the VW in this study, probably because of their special performance appeal and their lack of solid roof structures. For the larger domestic cars, the vehicles with serious or fatal injuries averaged about 5.5 percent, and the drivers with serious or fatal injuries about 4 percent. Further, the noncollision crashes for these cars were under 2 percent.

A high rate of noncollision crashes, such as occurs for VW and the Renault Dauphine, indicates some degree of handling instability. A noncollision crash occurs when the vehicle goes out of control, generally without the driver previously being aware that he is in difficulty. For the VW, many such crashes are rollovers. Although size may be an important factor in injuries resulting from collisions with other vehicles, there is no inherent reason that size should be an important factor causing handling instability in small cars.[27]

The Engineering Department of the Garden State Parkway in New Jersey has been keeping statistics on crashes in an effort to "examine the compatibility of the small car with the type and character of traffic using the Garden State Parkway—a limited access super highway." [28] Their report points out that "the majority of accidents on the Parkway are the simple, rear-end collisions. . . ."

Beetles accounted for slightly over 5 percent of the traffic on the Parkway and for about the same percentage of crashes. However, Beetles had nearly 7 percent of the serious injuries or fatalities. The spectrum of crashes for the VW was different also; nearly a quarter of the vehicles overturned, compared with about 5 percent rollover for all cars in the survey. Over 46 percent of the VW crashes involved only a single car, while 31.4 percent of all Parkway crashes were single-car crashes. Again, a control problem for the VW on high-speed roads is indicated.

The VW microbus fared even worse on the Parkway.

While the bus represented only 0.30 percent of the traffic on the Parkway, it was involved in 0.39 percent of the crashes and over one percent of those which resulted in serious or fatal injuries. Single-car crashes accounted for a whopping 71 percent of the VW microbus crashes.

The VW's poor record on crash survival is not confined to the United States. A study from Brisbane, Australia, of traffic collisions resulting in admissions to one of the hospitals in Queensland found that "Volkswagen was considerably over-represented in the accident series."[29] At the end of 1962, 3.6 percent of the vehicles registered in Queensland were Beetles. However, the crash statistics in this report show that 8.8 percent of the vehicles involved in injury-producing collisions in the study were VWs. Furthermore, although VW station wagons were only 0.6 percent of the total registrations, they comprised 2.6 percent of the total vehicles in collisions resulting in injury or death.

As in other studies, this report points out that for the VW, rollover occurred in most of the single-vehicle crashes, and ejection took place in nearly 80 percent of these.

The pattern which appears in these studies is that the VW is *significantly* more likely to produce serious or fatal injuries in a collision than an average car. In fact, except for the Renault Dauphine, the VW appears to be more likely to produce serious or fatal injuries than any of the foreign sedans of comparable size which have been studied. This statistic is even more surprising when one realizes that the VW does not seem to be involved in more crashes than would be expected on the basis of its registration figures. For example, the Registry of Motor Vehicles for the Commonwealth of Massachusetts reported that the VW accounted for 3.5 percent of the vehicles in that state in 1966, and 3.6 percent of the crashes, but they found that 6.4 percent of the fatal crashes involved the VW.[30]

In all of the above studies pertaining to Volkswagens in the United States in which statistics on age were presented, VW drivers were found to be younger than drivers of other vehicles:

| Name of Study | Percentage of Drivers under Age 30 In Volkswagen | Average of All Cars |
|---|---|---|
| ACIR (of VW accidents) | 65.5% | 46.0% |
| New York State VSDSS | 56.6% | 40.8% |
| Garden State Parkway | 67.5% | 45.2% |

Volkswagen of America has attempted to use this fact to excuse its poor record on injuries in VW crashes:

> National Safety Council data makes clear that younger drivers are more frequently involved in serious accidents than older drivers, and those under 25, as insurance rates demonstrate, are by far the most likely to be involved in serious accidents.[31]

The data to which Volkswagen of America is referring show that for the year 1968, 30.7 percent of all drivers in the United States were under 30, while these same drivers were associated with 45.7 percent of all fatal crashes occurring that year.[32]

These figures, however, have serious deficiencies. They do not, for example, take into account differences in annual mileage traveled by younger versus older drivers, or the fact that younger drivers are much more likely to drive small cars than older drivers. It may be a question of cause and effect: Do younger drivers have worse records, on their involvement in serious crashes, because they drive smaller cars, or do smaller cars have a worse record because their drivers are on average younger? There is indication in the data that smaller cars are more to blame.

The Cornell car-size study, for example, shows that small cars are much more likely to roll over in a crash, regardless of the age of the driver:[33]

| | Percentage of Cars Rolling Over in Accidents | |
|---|---|---|
| Driver Age | Small Cars (under 2000 lbs.) | Standard Cars (over 3000 lbs.) |
| Under 20 years | 61.8% | 28.0% |
| 20–29 years | 47.1% | 27.0% |
| 30–49 years | 45.2% | 17.4% |
| 50 years and over | 33.8% | 11.5% |

Although the cars of younger drivers do roll over more frequently than do those of older drivers, the effect of car size on the rollover percentage is more pronounced than is driver age. That is, the chances of a rollover are reduced more by an increase in car size (61.8 percent to 28 percent) than by an increase in driver age (61.8 percent to 33.8 percent).

The Campbell study tends to eliminate age as a factor by normalizing the conditions under which the crashes took place. That is, it defined 108 different possible classes of accidents which took into account car speed, site of impact on the car, and type of crash, so that the propensity of a particular make of car to be involved in a crash of a particular type did not contribute to his evaluation of the safety of the car in that accident. Yet Campbell's study shows that the Beetle is much more likely to inflict serious or fatal injury than the average automobile.

Several important conclusions emerge from the studies cited in this chapter. The first is that the Beetle's small size is itself a dangerous characteristic of the car. The high rate of injury caused by striking the VW windshield—which is very close to the driver and to a front-seat passenger—is caused by its size. The greater vulnerability of the VW when hit from the side is also a direct result of small size, since Volkswagen has increased interior space by making the doors and sides dangerously fragile.

Small size is supposed to have one compensating advantage: according to a prevailing myth, cars like the Beetle are less likely to become involved in accidents, because they are more maneuverable than large cars. This myth is not supported by the facts. At least in the case of Volkswagen vehicles, any reduction in collisions with other vehicles is more than made up for by an increased number of single-car crashes. When both collisions and single-car crashes are taken into account, the VW is involved in about as many crashes as would be expected from its numbers on the road.[34]

And once the Beetle crashes, the consequences—measured in terms of the frequency of serious or fatal occupant injury—are much more drastic than usual. All the studies that analyze factors contributing to the high injury rate in the Beetle cite the car's propensity to roll over in a crash and to eject its front-seat passengers, both very hazardous occurrences. (The causes of rollovers and ejection will be discussed in later chapters.) The Beetle also confers upon its owners a formidable set of other dangers, ranging from separation of the seats from their tracks, steering-wheel intrusion into the passenger compartment, and inadequate crush distance. Even within the inherent limitations of small size, the Beetle could be a much safer car in which to endure a collision, if VW wanted to make it safer. As it is, however, the Beetle's touted solidity is contradicted by the data of its performance in a crash.

# 2

## *Before the Crash: The Beetle's Erratic Dance*

The differences between the Beetle and more conventionally designed automobiles, both domestic and foreign, extend far beyond size and styling. The Beetle is rear-engined, in contrast to most American cars which have their engines in the front. Its suspension design is also radically different from that of other cars. These design features of the Beetle conspire with other features —fastback shape, small size, and light weight—to cause severe handling problems.

There are two major factors in vehicle handling: directional stability and control sensitivity. A car with a high degree of directional stability will tend to travel straight in whatever direction it is aimed. Ideally it will do this regardless of cross winds, bumps, or road camber (the technical term for road crowns or lateral grades). Control sensitivity, on the other hand, is a measure of the ability of a car to respond to its controls. A control-sensitive car will respond to the driver's steering commands as quickly and precisely as the road and tire traction permit.

An ideal car would have plenty of both directional stability and control sensitivity. The driver could be confident that the car would remain directionally stable regardless of what outside forces acted upon it, and at the same time know that the car would respond instantly to any steering maneuvers he needed to perform.

Available cars, of course, do not meet this ideal completely, but some do much better than others. The Citroën cars with Hydropneumatic suspension, for example, are directionally stable even in strong cross winds, and at the same time respond very quickly and accurately to steering maneuvers.

American auto makers have evolved suspension designs which are quite directionally stable, but which in many models are not very control sensitive.[1] This combination results largely from the attempt to satisfy the triple requirements of providing a soft, "boulevard" ride, keeping the cost of suspension systems low, and placing the engine in front.

The Beetle was designed in and for the Europe of the 1930s. In this pre-Autobahn era, the roads were narrow and winding, making a control-sensitive car desirable. But in attempting to satisfy this need, the designer of the Beetle created a car which had very little directional stability. Although its control sensitivity provided rapid response to steering, it was not precise—the car sometimes turned more sharply than the driver intended. In 1969, *Road & Track* magazine published a survey of owners of 1963–67 Beetles (whose suspension was only slightly modified from the original design).[2] Handling, implying control sensitivity, was listed by 17 percent of the owners as the best feature of the car. But the lack of directional stability was indicated by 27 percent of the owners, who listed side-wind sensitivity as the car's worst feature, and 13 percent, who listed the oversteering tendencies as the worst feature. In the conclusion of the survey, the editors stated that the Beetle's "strange road manners" were among its "obvious shortcomings." Jan Norbye, automotive editor for *Popular Science,* has written on the control problem of small cars:

> This is what produces single-vehicle accidents (statistically more prevalent among small cars). Cars go out of control because winds push them off course or because they lose their grip on the road. The car most prone to both phenomena is the rear-engined lightweight. It has less stability, on the straight and in cornering, than cars in the same weight class with front engines.[3]

The characteristics of the Beetle's handling which will be identified in this chapter as dangerous are (1) directional instability in cross winds; (2) oversteering behavior, particularly in cornering near the limits of tire adhesion; and (3) a propensity toward overturning during extreme maneuvers or after the impact of a crash. As these characteristics are discussed, it is important to realize that handling behavior grows out of a combination of several design features, none of which can be judged individually as good or bad. What is important is how well the engineers have set up a system of checks and balances to ensure the car's safe behavior.

### *Directional Instability in Cross Winds*

The most easily identified problem in the Beetle's handling is its extreme sensitivity. New drivers of the Beetle have reported that they must learn a whole new skill of steering in a zigzag to drive a straight line. More important, Beetles have been literally blown off the road by gusts of wind which affected ordinary cars only moderately.

The Beetle's cross-wind sensitivity is largely a product of its body shape and weight distribution. A cross wind will push any car sideways in the direction of the wind, but the body shape determines the point at which the wind pressure seems to concentrate its force. This point is called the "center of pressure." A cross wind not only pushes a car sideways, but also may *rotate* the car about its center of mass. If the center of pressure is behind the center of mass, the wind turns the car so that it is headed into the wind, and hence back toward its own path (Fig. 1d). If the center of pressure is ahead of the center of mass, as with the Beetle, the cross wind not only blows the car off course, but also turns the car so that it is headed further off course (Fig. 1c). Consequently, in cross winds the Beetle requires constant steering correction to keep it on course, as most drivers of the car know.

The instability of the Beetle in a cross wind has been investigated experimentally in scale-model wind-tunnel tests by Elmer Eugene Larrabee of the Massachusetts Institute of Technology. He notes that "some truck

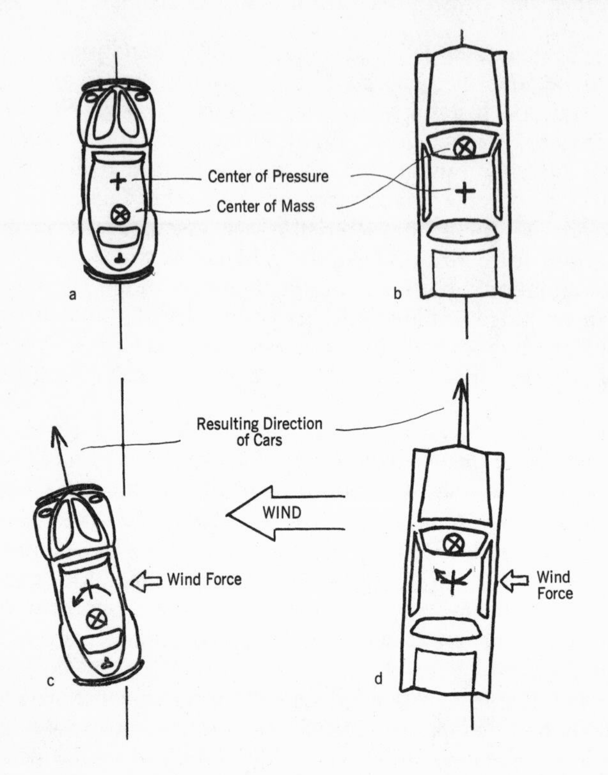


*Figure 1.* Directional instability in cross winds. The effect of a side wind on a car with its center of pressure ahead of its center of mass (a and c) and a car with its center of pressure behind its center of mass (b and d). Note that the VW requires a major steering correction to return it to its original path.

drivers hesitate to pass Volkswagens on narrow roads at high speeds for fear of disturbing the car to the extent that the driver may lose control." The tests he made tended to provide a basis for their fears:

> When the forward corner of the truck was abreast of the rear wheel of the Volkswagen sedan, the aerodynamic drag of the sedan was found to increase by 36%, corresponding to 1.6% of the weight of the car at a road speed of 60 mph. A side force of similar

magnitude was exerted, tending to push the Volkswagen away from the truck. . . . When the rear corner of the truck was slightly ahead of the sedan, somewhat smaller effects of the opposite sense were observed.[4]

*Oversteering Behavior*

Most Beetle owners note that when cornering at a sufficiently high speed, the rear end of the car feels as though it were slipping sideways, out of the turn. Thus the car points more sharply into the turn than the driver intended (Figure 2). This phenomenon is called "oversteer." Another way of describing a car which oversteers is to say that the faster one takes a given turn in such a car, the less he must turn the steering wheel to keep the car in the turn. If an oversteering car is cornered too fast, the rear tires can lose traction. The result is at least a momentary loss of control. The factors which cause the oversteering behavior of the VW are the suspension design and the placement of the engine at the back of the car, putting the greater portion of the car's weight on the rear wheels.

Every time a car turns a corner at high speed, centrifugal force tends to push the car away from the turn (Fig. 3a). Suspensions and tire factors being equiva-

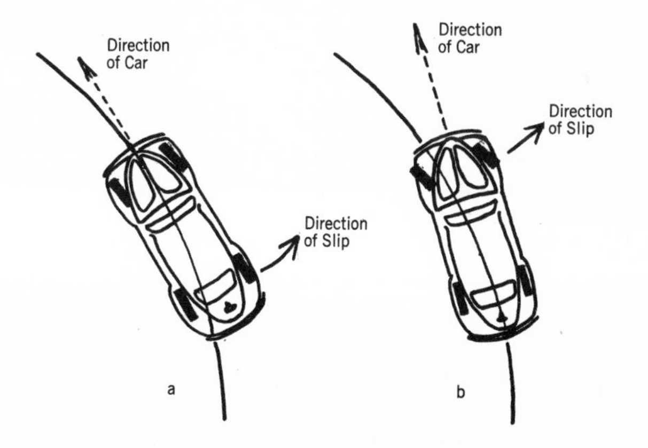


*Figure 2.* Oversteer/understeer. A VW oversteering in a corner (a) and understeering (b). Note the relative angles of the front wheels.

lent, in a front-engined car, where the center of mass is relatively far forward, the centrifugal force will pull the car out of the turn (understeer, Fig. 3b); but in a rear-engined car like the VW, the force on the center of mass will swing the tail out, pointing the front into the turn (oversteer, Fig. 3c). In each case (3b and 3c), the driver has to compensate for the centrifugal force by turning his wheels either more or less than the car has turned. The amount a tire "slips" side-

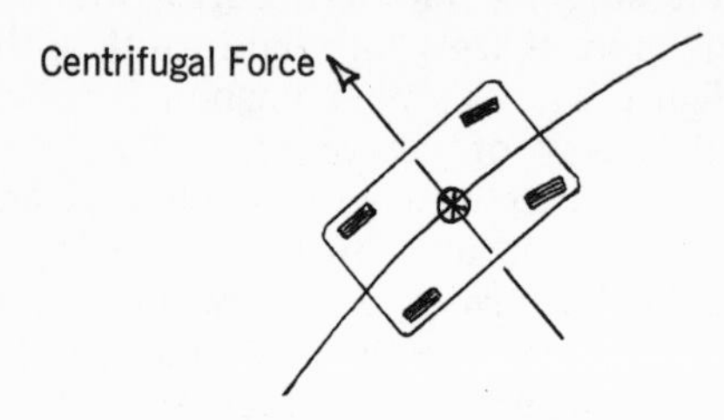


*Figure 3a.* Centrifugal force acting on a car, assuming the mass is concentrated at the center (⊕). Note that the centrifugal force acts perpendicular to the curve.

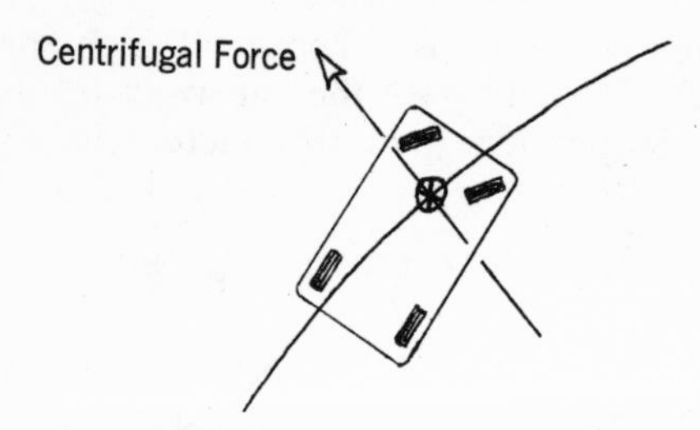


*Figure 3b.* Centrifugal force acting on a front-engined car.

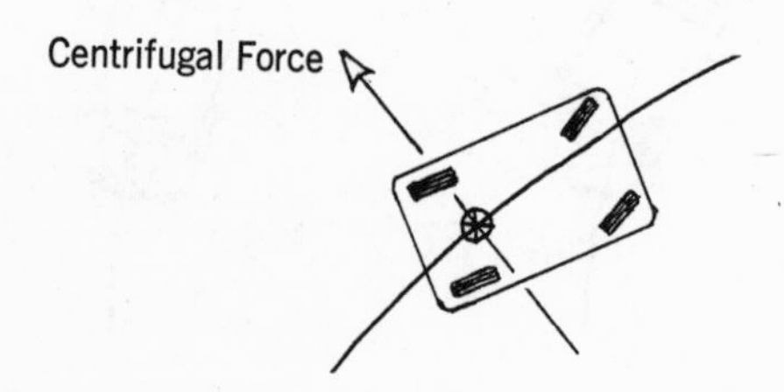


*Figure 3c.* Centrifugal force acting on a rear-engined car.

ways as a car turns a corner is measured by the angle between the actual direction the tire is traveling and the direction it would travel if there were no side force on it. This angle is called the "slip angle." *

When a Volkswagen oversteers in a turn—that is, when the rear slip angle becomes too great—the result can be total loss of control. Drivers who have experienced this, in recounting their experiences, often describe total frustration in trying to avoid a single-car crash. To solve this problem, which is caused by the greater weight on the Beetle's rear tires, VW recommends higher pressure in the rear tires than in the front. By firming up the rear tires, their traction is improved and their tendency to slip out of the turn (thus forcing the nose of the car too far into the turn) is diminished. This

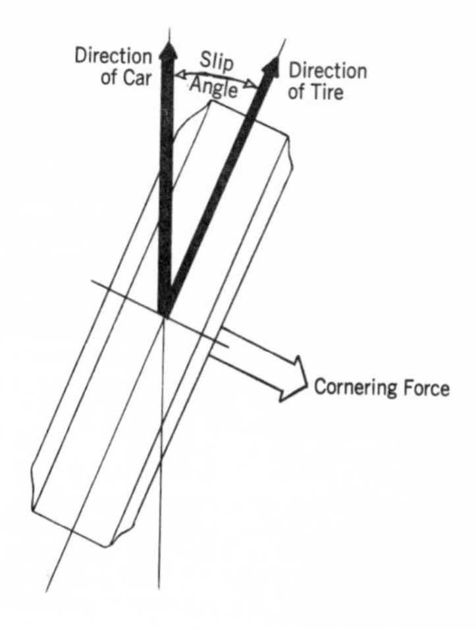


*Figure 4.* Slip angle. The circumstances depicted would result from a car turning to the right so that the centrifugal forces push the tire to the left.

* The slip angle increases as side force on the tire increases (Fig. 4). If a corner is negotiated at too high a speed, the traction of a tire may be insufficient to counteract the side force and the tire will begin to skid. Oversteer and its opposite, understeer, can be defined in terms of tire-slip angles. The rear tires on a car that is oversteering will have a larger slip angle than the front tires. That is, the rear tires will slip sideways more than the front tires, in effect steering the car more sharply into the turn. If a car is understeering, its front tires will have the larger slip angle, and the steering effect of the front tires will be diminished.

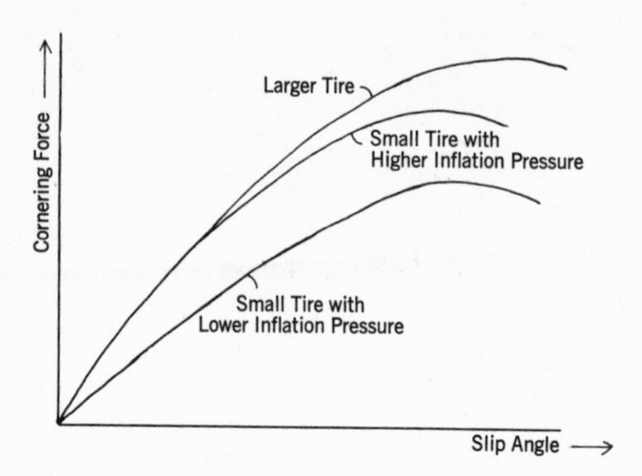


*Figure 5.* Cornering force *vs.* slip angle. Higher pressure in a tire will increase its cornering force up to a point, but larger tires are necessary to give greater cornering force at large slip angles.

remedy, however, is far from satisfactory. In the first place, few drivers are aware that VW rear tires should be kept at higher pressures than the front tires. Moreover, few gas station attendants—upon whom the driver relies—realize how critical this is. Finally, there is a limit to the effectiveness of using higher pressures to keep the car in the turn (Figure 5). A better way to compensate for the VW's dangerous cornering behavior is to use a carefully chosen larger size of tires in back, as rear-engined racing cars do. But this is generally considered to be impractical in passenger cars because it would make tire rotation and safe use of a single spare tire impossible.

As noted above, the position of the center of mass is not the only factor which causes oversteer in the Beetle; the design of the suspension is the other main factor. VW has tried a few suspension modifications to compensate for the instability that results from the heavier weight in the rear of the car. However, not until the 1968 model had the Beetle undergone more than slight changes in its suspension since its original prototype of the early thirties. Even these changes, while improvements, have not been enough.

Both the front and rear suspensions of the Beetle are of the trailing-link type, so called because the wheel connections to the suspension linkages trail behind the linkage connections to the frame. The front suspension

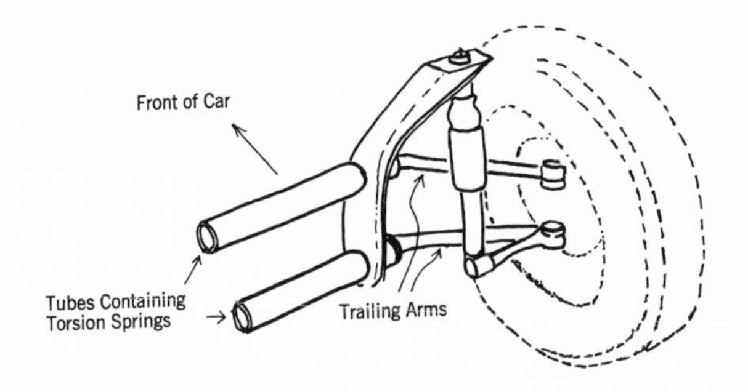


*Figure 6*. Beetle front suspension.

has double trailing links on each side (Figure 6). These links hold the front wheels in such a way that their camber (vertical tilt) does not change with respect to the body as the wheels move up and down. Thus as the car leans or rolls in a corner, its front tires lean with it, and change camber with respect to the road. In 1959 an anti-roll bar was added to the front suspension, and there have been a few other minor changes. This same suspension is still in use, however, in the ordinary Beetles. The Super Beetle, introduced in 1971, has a MacPherson strut front suspension, but since the Consumer Union's tests showed little handling or ride improvement over the double trailing arm suspension, the change was probably made primarily to gain additional trunk space and a smaller turning radius.

On all models up through 1972, a single trailing arm is used on the rear suspension to locate each swing axle longitudinally. The swing axles are connected to the differential by universal joints, which can be bent at various angles while transmitting power to the rear wheels. On all models up through 1967, the outer ends of the swing axles are bolted rigidly to the wheels (Fig. 6). The result of this arrangement is that as the rear wheels rise with respect to the body, they lean inward (*negative camber*) and toe inward (the front of the tire points toward the center of the car). As the rear wheels move downward, they lean outward (*positive camber*) but also toe inward. On 1968 models with automatic clutches,* and on all 1969 and later models, universal

* Volkswagen's misnomer for its automatic clutch is Automatic Stick Shift.

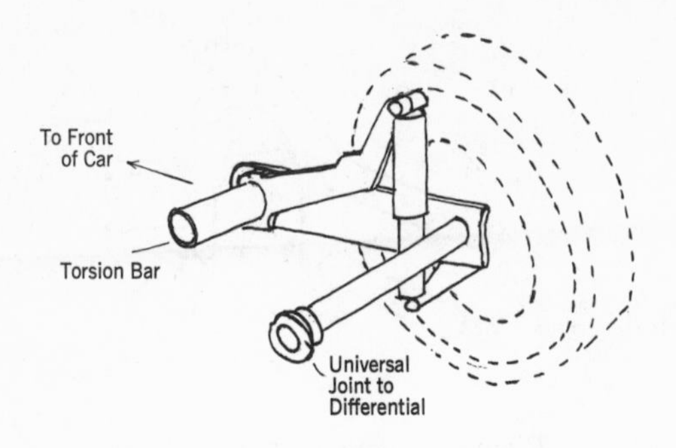


*Figure 7.* VW swing axle rear suspension.

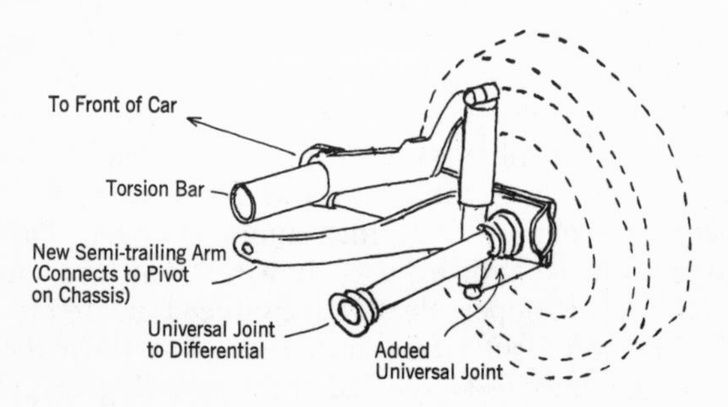


*Figure 8.* VW double-jointed rear suspension.

joints were also placed at the outboard ends of the axles along with modified semi-trailing arms (Fig. 8). This addition reduces the amount of camber change in the rear wheels as they move up and down and eliminates the toeing-in (Fig. 9).

Camber change is another way in which suspension affects tire traction and slip angle. A slight negative camber of the outside wheel gives the lowest slip angle—and therefore the greatest traction and control—for a given cornering force and weight. Too much negative camber, however, will increase the slip angle of a tire, as will any positive camber.

In a swing axle rear suspension, camber can change in two ways. First, drastic changes occur as the rear end goes over bumps, because the wheels rise and fall with

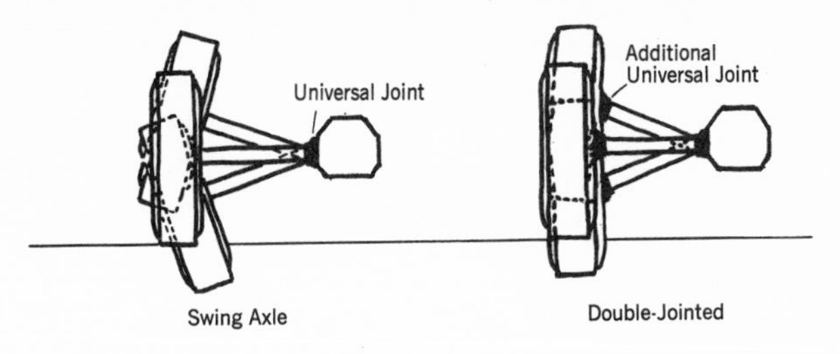


*Figure 9.* Up and down wheel movements in VW rear suspensions.

respect to the body (Fig. 9). Second, and more important, are the camber variations when the rear end of the car is lifted.

Since the rear wheels are rigidly connected to their axles, when the car is cornering the force of the road on a tire mounted on a swing axle translates to an upward or downward force on the axles. The axles, in turn, transmit this force to the differential, which is rigidly connected to the frame of the car. The wheel and axle on the outside of the turn push upward, while on the inside they pull downward. These up and down forces are not equal, however, since the outside tire (whose axle pushes up) is more heavily loaded than the inside tire (Fig. 10). The net result is to lift the rear of the car in a corner. The technical term for this is "jacking." The jacking effect is self-promoting since the higher the rear end is lifted, the more leverage the outside wheel and axle have. The jacking of the rear end produces a positive camber in both rear wheels (they tilt outward at the top). This means that the rear wheels lose even more traction, exacerbating the oversteering tendencies due to the excess weight in the rear. What happens is that as traction on the rear tires is reduced, they are less able to resist the centrifugal force that, in a VW or other rear-engined car, swings the rear out of the turn and points the nose into it.

The other way in which the Beetle suspension affects oversteer is more subtle. In a corner, some of a car's weight is lifted from the wheels on the inside of the turn and added to the outside wheels (Fig. 11). The

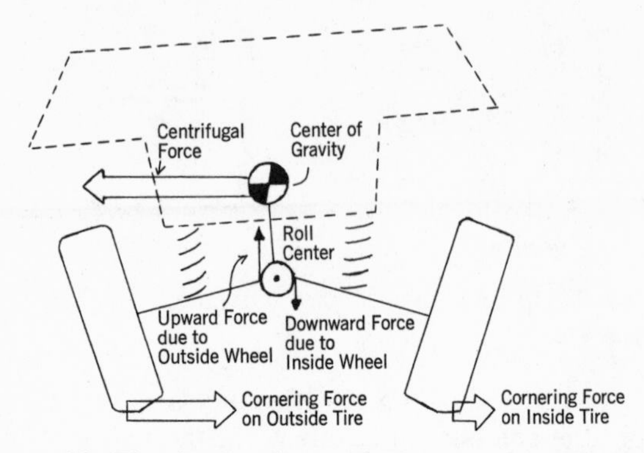


*Figure 10.* The forces that contribute to jacking. Note the positive camber of both wheels. Cornering force is greater on the outside tire because it has more weight on it.

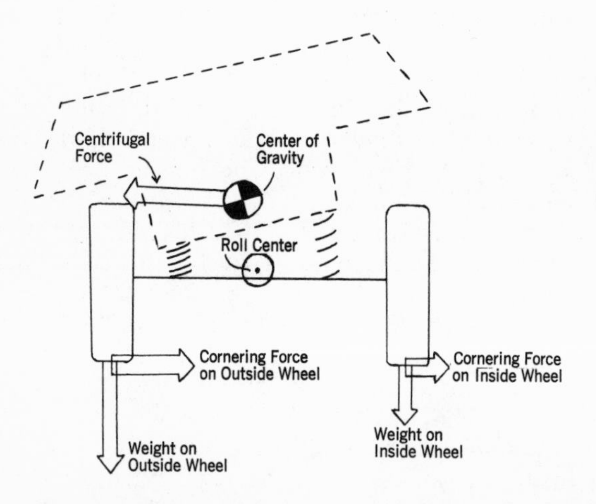


*Figure 11.* The forces that contribute to weight transfer. Note that the greater the weight on a tire, the greater its cornering force.

total amount of weight transferred is proportional to the centrifugal force, the height of the center of gravity of the car, and the narrowness of the track. Because of the relatively high center of gravity and narrow track of the Beetle, its weight transfer is greater than on a typical American sedan in a given corner at the same speed.

The portion of the total weight transfer across each axle is a function of the design of the suspension system. The roll axis of a car is an imaginary axis going lengthwise through the car, and about which the car rotates when it is pushed sideways. The higher the roll axis at an axle, the greater the weight transfer across that axle. In addition, the height of the roll axis affects traction, in that if the weight transfer is sufficiently high, the outside tire will be overloaded and will not be able to develop enough cornering force to keep that axle in the turn.[5] The design of the VW suspension system is such that the roll axis is at ground level at the front, but nearly a foot off the ground at the rear (Fig. 12). This is just the opposite of what is needed to counteract the oversteering tendencies of the car. The later Beetles with double-jointed rear axles and a MacPherson-type front suspension have a somewhat higher front roll axis, and lower rear roll axis.

Also, in order to change the proportion of weight transfer across each axle, special springs can be used which couple the motion of wheels on the same axle. These springs alter the car's resistance (called the "roll stiffness") to rotating about its roll axis.

When VW finally attempted to improve the car's handling, it first tried using special springs to vary the front and rear roll stiffness. One of the simplest of these devices is an anti-roll bar, a simple torsion bar placed transversely between the wheels and connected to the lower torsion arms. If one wheel moves up or down, this bar tends to pull the other wheel in the same direction. Volkswagens built after the 1959 model year were equipped with such a bar on the front to increase the front slip angle, thus decreasing oversteer. The roll stiffness of the rear suspension of the Beetle was de-

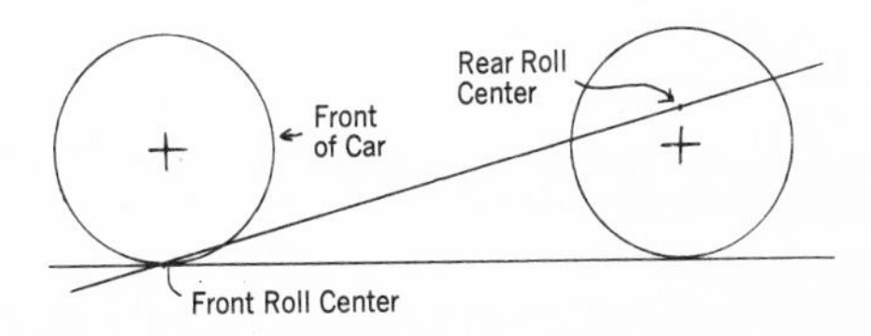


*Figure 12.* Roll axis. It runs longitudinally along the middle of the car.

creased in the 1967 models by adding an extra torsion bar between the rear wheels. This spring, unlike the anti-roll bar, helps support the car so that the regular rear springs can be less stressed, but it does not contribute to the roll stiffness as do the regular torsion bars which are connected to the trailing arms. The resulting decrease in rear roll stiffness gives better rear traction, further reducing oversteer, at least at moderate cornering speeds. But the problem is still severe near the upper limits of cornering traction. Ironically, the effects of these corrections are so strong that recent VWs actually understeer rather severely in moderate cornering; yet, during harder cornering, the heavy rear end can overpower all the corrective measures; the rear end suddenly slides sideways, and serious oversteer results.

All of the above discussion has been concerned with cornering at constant speed and radius. Some of these factors become much worse when there are changes in steering or car speed. For example, going into a sudden turn causes the body to roll more than it would moving steadily in the same turn. This transient behavior may be sufficient to cause a loss of control even though the cornering speed may not be too high, because the suspension geometry and loading can change rapidly. If the car is braked while negotiating a turn, the resultant transfer of weight from the rear to the front promotes jacking in the Beetles with swing axles. Thus, a Beetle may seem to be cornering safely within its adhesion limits, but if the driver puts on the brakes to avoid any obstacles, the car may suddenly go out of control.

It may seem curious that for a rear-engined car like the Beetle—which has a built-in tendency to oversteer—the designer incorporated such oversteer-increasing features as a swing axle suspension (with its high roll center) and a front suspension with a low roll center. The design's longevity seems almost a quirk of history. Part of that history was given by Jan Norbye:

> The case of Dr. Ferdinand Porsche (1875–1951) is most interesting. When he designed the Auto Union V-16 racing car in 1933, . . . he guessed wrong about the roll center height of his trailing arm and torsion bar front suspension. . . .
>
> He felt that roll would be practically nonexistent

> with a center of gravity at approximately the same level as the springs. Olley was soon to divulge that trailing arm systems give a roll center exactly at ground level—with absolutely zero roll stiffness, but only after Dr. Porsche had experienced the unpleasant surprise of seeing considerable roll and alarming front wheel camber angles when testing of the Auto Union began. As a result of his miscalculations in the suspension geometry, the car had vicious roadholding. By the end of its first racing season, 1934, Dr. William Werner, Auto Union's director of engineering, was ready to scrap the Porsche design and start from scratch. But he was overruled. Meanwhile, Dr. Porsche had laid down the Volkswagen while still laboring under the same misconception.[6]

Dr. Porsche's "misconceptions" were also allowed to stand in the Volkswagen design until 1968, although engineers knew the problem three decades before. They simply assumed—or hoped—that the car would operate at relatively low speeds, so that the potentially dangerous handling would not be a problem. Their hopes proved tragically unfounded.

*Rollover*

Because the likelihood of ejection is so great, the propensity of the Beetle to roll over probably kills more people than any other VW handling problem. The ACIR report on the Volkswagen, discussed in detail in Chapter 1, documents the Beetle's high incidence of overturning in crashes.[7] Overall, the Cornell study found that in their sample of crashes there was a rollover rate of about 18 percent in domestic cars. Volkswagens, however, overturned at a rate of 41 percent. So in more than two out of five accidents, Beetles overturned, more than double the rate for domestic cars. The ratio of rollovers without collisions to the total number of crashes studied was nearly four times as large for the Beetle as for large domestic cars. More than a quarter of all the rural, injury-producing crashes involved rollover without a collision. The report states:

> This strongly suggests that improvement in the rollover stability of the vehicle, by whatever means, might prevent many accidents from occurring and, in consequence, prevent injury as well. This may be the greatest

> single safety improvement that Volkswagen can effect, because door opening and occupant ejection, which increase the risk of serious injury, occur most frequently in rollover accidents.[8]

The Cornell report dealt with the pre-1968–69 type of Beetle with swing axle suspensions. Jacking is no longer a problem with jointed rear suspensions. The Beetle still has a high center of gravity and narrow track, both of which can make the car less stable against rollover. Also, the strong oversteering in emergency maneuvers can set the car sliding sideways so that any obstruction or hole in the road can "trip" the car and start it rolling.

A VW can be rolled over on a completely smooth surface. By contrast, it is nearly impossible to turn over an American car on a smooth surface. Friedrich Goes, Volkswagen's first safety director, when asked whether a Beetle could be overturned on an ordinary piece of concrete pavement without striking an object, testified under oath:

> Yes, you can, by inducing—let's see, which movement is it? It's a roll oscillation. If you apply a roll oscillation to the car in the right amount at the right time then you can overroll the Volkswagen.
> . . . you have to do a fishtailing maneuver so that the car body is rolling to the right side when the car is skidding to the right side as well.[9]

Compounding the rollover problem in Beetles built before mid-1968 is a design defect that is absolutely inexcusable. As the cornering force on a turning Beetle, or any car, increases, the wheels incur increasing side loads which, in effect, try to pull the *tire* into the center of the *wheel,* causing an "airout." If, for instance, a car is turning left and the right tires suddenly air out, the car will fall suddenly over towards its right side and this may induce rollover.

Airout is easily prevented by safety wheel rims, which were patented in 1940 by C. H. Sauer.[10] A safety rim incorporates "safety humps" running circumferentially around the rim to retain the tire bead more securely as shown in Figure 13. The safety rim reduces the chance

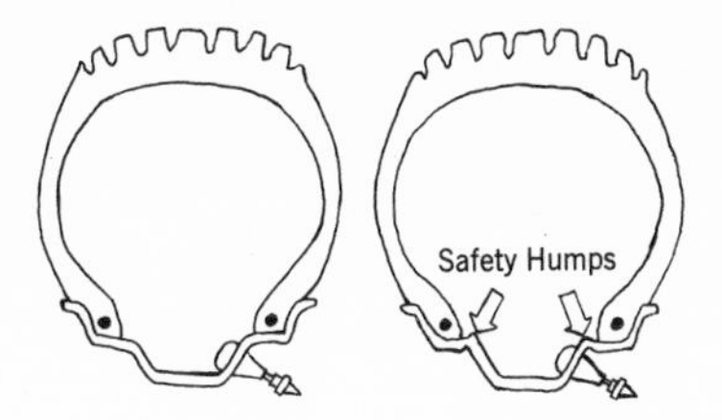


*Figure 13.* Comparison of old wheel rim with newer safety rim. Note "safety humps." Greater force is required to press the tire bead (a rubber-encased steel cable that gives rigidity to the tire) from the rim shoulder on the safety rim. Adapted from the *Volkswagen Service Manual.*[13]

of an airout—which occurs when air is suddenly lost from a tubeless tire because of the unseating of the tire bead. An airout generally occurs under severe side loads such as hard cornering. In addition, the safety rim helps retain the tire carcass on the rim after a blowout or puncture. Tire retention is very important in a blowout because the vehicle can be more easily controlled while it is being brought to a stop.[11]

The patent on safety rims passed into the public domain in 1957, but Volkswagen delayed the incorporation of safety rims on the Beetle until 1968—more than ten years beyond that date. The price to Volkswagen for the incorporation of this design would only have been the cost for retooling its rim dies. Volkswagen's delay in equipping its vehicles with safety rims is a prime example of scrimping on safety.

The *Volkswagen Workshop Manual 1969,* which does not come with the car and is not generally available to owners, makes the following comment about safety rims:

> The rim of Type 1 and 3 is of the safety type with a hump to prevent the tire from being forced into the rim well under extreme operating conditions, e.g. fast cornering.[12]

The *VW Service Manual* contains a special warning about radial ply tires and non-safety rims.

> The tubeless radial ply tires may only be used with the hump type rims because the normal rims do not offer

> sufficient support to the tire beads. It is permissible to install tubes in these tires if the vehicle is to be used on very bad roads or in off-road conditions.
>
> If owners of vehicles with normal rims produced prior to production date October 10, 1967, chassis no. 118 227 175, wish to install radial tires, inner tubes *must* be used [emphasis in original].[14]

Volkswagen introduced tubeless tires as original equipment beginning with the 1957 model year. However, the VW owner's manual provided with the car does not mention any potential hazards associated with the 1957–1968 model Beetles which have these tubeless tires.[15] The safety rim wheel was introduced in mid-production of the 1968 models with chassis number 118,227,175 (See Appendix IV for an explanation of VW's vehicle number system). These safety rims have four bolt holes and are not interchangeable with the five bolt pattern used on the 1957–1968 VWs. Although adapters could be produced,[16] Volkswagen should produce safety rim wheels with the old five bolt pattern and provide them, mounted and balanced, at no charge to all owners of the 1957–1968 Beetles. The addition of tubes to the non-safety rim wheels would help prevent airout, but such a retrofit is *not* an adequate solution since it would not alleviate the problem of the tire carcass coming off the wheel in the event of a blowout or puncture.

*Handling in the Super Beetle*

To answer the question whether the latest Super Beetle offers any major improvements over its predecessors, we quote from the latest test of that model by Consumers Union. "The model that Volkswagen calls the *Super Beetle* feels little different from the many unsuper Beetles CU has tested. . . . Our *Super Beetle* rode better than have our earlier Beetles, thanks to a redesigned front suspension. But it was still among the worst-riding cars in this test group." The test group contained the Datsun PL510, the Vega, the Toyota Corona, the Pinto, and the Gremlin. However, a good ride is only one of the qualities which an adequate suspension system should possess; handling, especially in emergency situations, is certainly more crucial. Of the handling under severe conditions, CU found:

> CU's drivers had a time of it trying to stay in their lane at high speeds when the car was buffetted [*sic*] by gusty crosswinds.
>
> In emergency maneuvers, the *Super Beetle* eventually reached a point of instability. The car normally tends to turn a bit less sharply than you'd expect from the angle of the front wheels; engineers call that understeer. During hard cornering the *VW's* understeer sometimes became severe; the car tended to plow straight ahead, even with the wheels turned. On the other hand, the car sometimes switched to oversteer (with the rear end swinging wider than was intended). The oversteer, though disconcerting, could be controlled by turning the steering wheel briefly in the opposite direction. Response was quick but fairly unpredictable, earning the *VW* a judgment of fair-to-poor for its emergency handling.[17]

The Super Beetle, then, despite its new type of front suspension, still has the most serious of the normal Beetle's problems. The severe understeering is the result of VW's repeated attempts to correct the car's basic oversteering tendency, but in emergency maneuvers when predictability is needed most, the corrective measures fail. Unfortunately there are no simple cures for the deficiencies of the Volkswagen suspension system. Bolt-on devices such as the camber compensator have not been proved to be as effective as is claimed. In fact, the only bolt-on device which can be confidently recommended is the front anti-roll bar which is installed on all post-1959 models. Retrofitting of a rear torsion bar of the type added in 1967 is not such a simple task as the effectiveness of the bar depends on reducing the stress in the main torsion bars.

### *Other Volkswagen Models*

The suspension designs for the VW microbus and the VW Type III (Squareback and Fastback) show the strong family resemblance to the Beetle that exists between, for example, all American Ford products. The original Type III suspension was virtually identical to its contemporary Beetle (double trailing arm front suspension, and trailing arm swing axle rear suspension). Double-jointed rear axles were adopted on the Type III for the 1968 models, and in 1970, the MacPherson front suspension was adopted. As one might expect, the handling of the Type III is very similar to that of a similarly suspended Beetle. A Consumers Union test of the 1969 Squareback noted that "gusty crosswinds blew the car off course too suddenly and too easily at freeway speeds," and that "driven very fast through tight turns, the *Squareback* first understeered, then suddenly began to oversteer, though not to a dangerous degree, in our judgment." [18]

The microbus has not only all the faults of the Beetle, but adds a few of its own. First, its boxy shape makes it far more vulnerable to crosswinds. Second, the rear wheels are given added leverage for jacking in that reduction gears are added to the outboard ends of the rear axles in such a way that the wheel centerline is below the axle centerline by several inches. In 1968, along with a general body redesign, the suspension system was changed to the double-jointed rear axle–MacPherson strut front axle type. Although this made some improvement, the handling of the bus, as reported by *Consumer Reports,* is still sensitive to side winds. They also noted:

> In high-speed emergency maneuvers, the *VW's* front end at first ran wider and wider through the corners, and steering effort increased considerably. Then, without warning, the rear stepped sideways. That, of course, required quick and skillful steering correction. Nor did that disconcerting behavior occur only during very hard cornering. We ran our high speed handling tests about 10 to 20 mph slower than usual—mainly because the *VW* lacked the power to go any faster.[19]

In order to keep the Beetle from being even worse than it normally is, it must be kept in excellent mechanical condition. All joints in both the front and rear suspensions should be checked at the time of recommended front-end lubrication (every 1500 miles) for excessive play, and to be sure that all protective rubber boots are intact. Engineers at the Cornell Aeronautical Laboratory have suggested that the rear suspension trailing links be checked, too. "Under severe conditions (frequent off-the-road driving) the spring plates have been known to break due to the constant flexing." [20] The engine and transmission mounts should be checked both for corrosion of the metal parts and for deterioration of the rubber parts. The brakes should be inspected and tested to insure that they operate smoothly and evenly, and do not pull to one side. Wheel alignment is critically important for safety in the Beetle. Worn shock absorbers can exacerbate transient behavior. They should be checked every several thousand miles, and replaced, if necessary, with heavy duty units.

Tires are as important as suspension components in the Beetle's handling. The Beetle is exceptionally sensitive to poor quality or badly worn tires. Worn tires should be replaced well before they are bald (when there are at least two 32nds of an inch of tread left). As replacement tires, radial tires such as the Michelin X should be seriously considered, but they must be mounted on safety rims or inner tubes must be used. Radial tires reduce the slip angles for a given weight and cornering force, and they are less affected by camber change than conventional tires. (*Under no circumstances, however, should radial tires be mixed with non-radial tires on a car.*) Regardless of the type of tire used, rear tire pressure must be kept 30 to 50 percent higher than front tire pressure. Tire pressure several pounds higher than is recommended by Volkswagen (maintaining the 30–50 percent front-rear difference) might improve handling although the ride may become consequently more harsh.

Somewhat wider wheel rims (five inches wide, perhaps) may also help traction. If the non-safety rims are replaced, it should be with wider safety-type rims. We cannot recommend reversed rims, in which the outer part of the rim is removed and replaced backwards on the center to widen the track of the car, because they will significantly alter the steering geometry, and because they place a portion of the tire tread outside the fenders.

If the car is generally lightly loaded (no more than two passengers and no luggage in the rear of the car), reducing the height of the rear suspension by partially unloading the rear torsion bars is a fairly inexpensive method of reducing the oversteer and the likelihood of jacking. This should be done only by a professional mechanic.

Even if these changes are effected, however, it must be remembered that the handling of the Beetle is basically treacherous, and inexpensive modifications cannot improve the handling characteristics in any fundamental way. Therefore it is crucial that drivers be aware of the Beetle's precarious handling. Volkswagen commissioned Arthur D. Little, Inc., to analyze the Garden State Parkway studies and some of the findings were:

> We suggest . . . that VW continue to watch the turnover problem. Steps against turnover should include both statistical and engineering studies—and design improvements based thereon. . . . We also recommend that VW owner manuals include cautions on driver technique appropriate to the oversteering characteristics of the VW.[21]

However, Volkswagen has not included such cautions in its owner manuals and has never admitted there are handling problems in the Beetle.

# 3

## *During the Crash: Ejection*

### The VW Ejector Seat: Out the Rear Window

In 1969 UCLA engineering students guided by engineers from the Institute of Transportation and Traffic Engineering [1] crashed a 1967 Ford Custom sedan into the rear end of a fully instrumented 1969 Beetle which contained two full-sized male dummies in the front seats, and two smaller dummies in the rear seat. The Ford was driven at 30 mph, the VW was stationary.

On impact, the dummy in the driver's seat pitched backward, causing the seat back to fail. The dummy then slid backward until its head struck the chest of the dummy directly behind the driver. The dummy in the right front position occupied a specially strengthened VW seat. During the crash, the seat failed and the dummy experienced severe whiplash.

The left rear dummy, simulating the size of a 13-year-old, slid along the collapsed seat back, and hit the rear window which popped out without breaking. The dummy's head and shoulders cleared the opening and its head struck the hood of the Ford. The right rear dummy was also hurtled rearward and partially out of the rear window opening which the left rear dummy had broken. The right rear dummy's head also struck the hood of the Ford.

In a confidential memo to its dealers, VW described the results of the study as follows:

> A test on VW seats in *rear-end collisions was conducted by UCLA* in 1969. VWoA provided cars for the test and they were "rear-ended" by 1967 full-size Fords at 30 mph. The back of the VW front seat bent rearward about 30°, but *the seat did not leave the track* [emphasis in original].[2]

This is hardly an accurate description of what happened. The erroneous impression is left that the VW seats performed adequately. VWoA fails to explain that the seat that tilted 30° was the reinforced one, and that serious injuries would have resulted from the tilt of the seat back alone. Nor does the company mention any of the other results.

In an automobile, the driver's seat must not only be comfortable, to minimize driver fatigue, and adjustable, so that all drivers can use it, but it and all seats must remain stationary and reasonably rigid in a crash. Moreover, the seat back, should it yield to the forces generated by a crash, must yield in a controlled fashion to help protect against whiplash. These are the most important requirements of automobile seat design, and Volkswagen apparently ignored both of them, at least through the 1970 models. Crashes in which the Beetle is rear-ended have made clear two VW seat design deficiencies.[3]

The frame of the Beetle seat back is a steel tube shaped like an inverted "U." The bottom ends of this tube are attached to the centers of the seat's adjustment runners. About eight inches higher up, the tube rests against tabs on the back of the lower seat frame. When a Beetle is hit from behind, or when the car spins out and smashes tail-first into an object, the occupants of the front seats are shoved back hard against the upper parts of the seat backs. When this happens, the seat-back frame rest becomes a pivot point, and the seat-back frame acts like a lever, and, if the forces are strong enough, will wrench the seat runner upward and off its track (see Figure 1). The seat is no longer attached to any part of the car, and the occupant, even if he is wearing seat belts, is unrestrained and can be thrown backward against the top of the rear seat, the window frame, or out the rear window. Moreover, the seat itself is free to move about in the passenger compartment and can in-

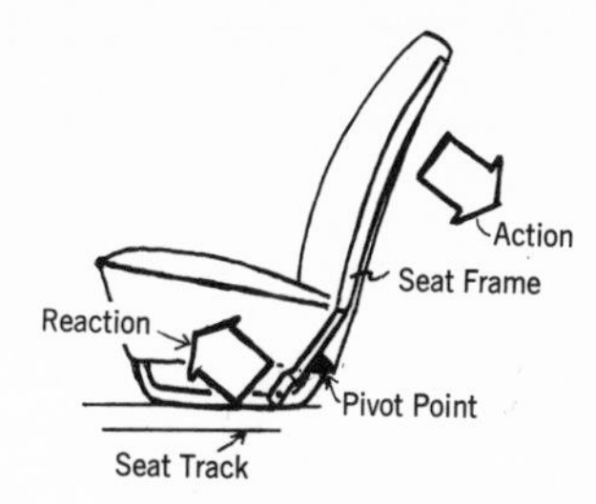


*Figure 1.* Forces on a seat when VW is struck from rear. The force of the passenger against the seat back results in an upward force on the seat bottom. The effect of the force is to push the lower rails up and out of their tracks.

jure other passengers or throw its occupant against hard surfaces inside the car.

It is possible for the seat to come loose so easily because the seat runner and track are too weak to withstand the large, concentrated forces exerted by the seat-back frame (see Figure 2). The lever effect of the seat-back frame multiplies the force of the occupant on the seat several times. A force in excess of 1,000 pounds would be exerted on each seat runner in a crash of a Beetle with a 150-pound occupant in the seat, if it were rear-ended by a full-sized American car at 30 mph.[4]

A second design deficiency in the Beetle front seats is the weakness of the seat back itself. The same dynamic forces which cause the seat runner to be torn from the seat track can, in some cases, bend the seat-back frame about the point where it rests on the lower seat frame. When this happens, the seat back reclines,

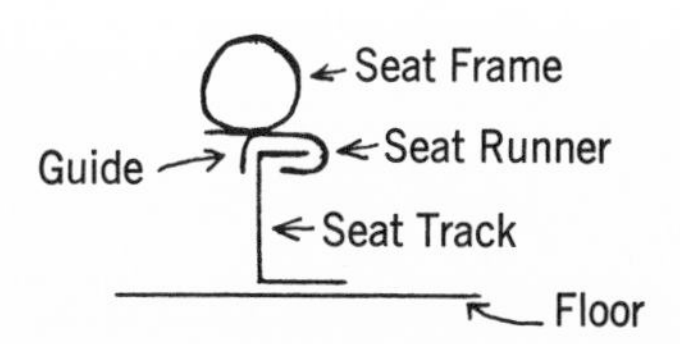


*Figure 2.* Pre-1971 VW seat track. This simplified sectional diagram (not to scale) was supplied to the Center for Auto Safety by VWoA.

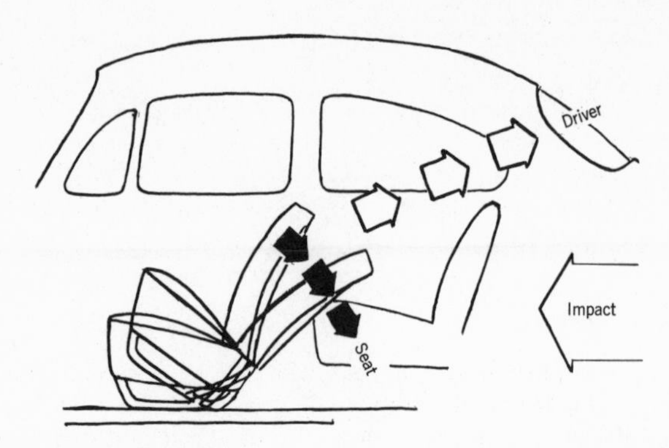


*Figure 3.* Ejection through the rear window. This can occur if the VW is struck from the rear while standing still, or if it spins out at high speeds and crashes into something while traveling backward. The driver and/or passenger can be hurtled toward the rear of the car, where he may hit the window frame or continue partially or completely through the rear window.

becoming a sliding board which allows the occupant to move backward without restraint (see Figure 3). Again, the occupant will either collide with the inside of the rear of the car, or he will be thrown out through the rear window. Seat belts are of little use in this case since the occupant can slide backward under the belt unhindered.

These two seat defects are interrelated. When a VW is impacted from the rear, generally only one failure will occur; either the seat back will recline or the whole seat will be torn from the car. All Beetles from 1959 through 1970 are seriously affected by these seat defects. There are no crash statistics yet available from which to determine whether or not the post-1970 Beetle and Super Beetle seat design is any less unsafe than its predecessors.

A report from the Department of Transportation-funded Multidisciplinary Accident Investigation Program and other crash reports [5] show that the seats in the Squareback and Fastback VW may also be weak. According to the DOT report, a stationary 1968 VW Squareback was rear-ended by a 1967 Ford Galaxie which was traveling about 25 mph. "Vehicle #2's driver's seat was almost completely displaced from its floor mounted anchor." [6] The failure of the seat tracks in a 1965 Squareback led to a lawsuit in Hawaii in which a $25,200 judgment was awarded to the plaintiff against VWAG.[7]

In letters to the Center for Auto Safety, dated March 11 and March 15, 1971, Volkswagen of America's Vice President Arthur R. Railton described changes which have been made in the Beetle's seats and seat anchorages as follows:

> In April 1962, vertical guides were added to the seat frame runners. In June 1962, the seat runners were reinforced. In November 1962, the spring was strengthened in the seat-adjustment control. In August 1964, the runner ratchet was strengthened. In 1965, the seat backs were fitted with a locking device, and additional reinforcement was added to the runners and an apron was added to prevent seat belts from being damaged by the runners. In 1966, the seat-back lock was moved to the backrest side panel. In 1969, a spring-loaded forward stop was added to the seat track and a new attachment point for backrest was added to the seat frame. In 1970, the seat track was redesigned to provide greater strength and ease of adjustment.

Several of these changes in seat design—notably moving the seat-back lock—have nothing to do with strengthening the seat. Others—like adding the seat lock in the first place, the vertical guides on the seat frame runners, the apron to prevent seat belts from contacting the runners, and the spring-loaded forward stop—have nothing to do with seat safety in a rear-end collision. For the others, it is impossible to tell whether the changes amounted to actual improvements. No precise figures as to the degree of strengthening are provided. (Indicating the number of changes in the Beetle without indicating their quality or effectiveness, a numbers game without meaningful numbers, is typical of much of VW's advertising.) One of the changes noted by Mr. Railton deserves specific comment. A modification to strengthen the seat tracks was not made until 1970 (effective on 1971 models). However, integral head restraints were introduced in 1968 Beetles. This safety feature—it protects against whiplash—increases the height of the seat and compounds the problem of seat track weakness by providing extra leverage, thus increasing the forces which tend to separate the seat runners.

Three studies have evaluated the performance of VW seats in crashes. Two of them deal primarily with seat failures resulting from *frontal* impacts. The third—the UCLA study described at the beginning of this chapter—gave evidence of seat failure in rear impacts. Because of the peculiar leverage effect of the VW Beetle seat-back frame bar, which operates only in rear-end impacts, studies dealing with frontal crashes cannot adequately delineate the seat defects described in this report. *Yet Volkswagen of America has cited these studies as confirming the safety of the Beetle seat design,* without pointing out that the conclusions of two of the reports are essentially irrelevant to the problem of the adequacy of VW seats in crashes in which the VW is struck in the rear end.[8]

The first report is Cornell Aeronautical Laboratory's *Study of Volkswagen Accidents in the United States.* This study detected little difference in the frequency of seat track damage in frontal impacts between the VW and other cars in the study. Although damage to Volkswagen's seat tracks occurred more frequently in rear impacts, Cornell made no comparison between VWs and other vehicles on this point. In rear impacts the VW seats were torn free of the tracks in about a quarter of the cases, and some track damage occurred in half of all rear-end collisions. The report added:

> The recent introduction of seat back locking devices, although desirable in preventing the seat back from folding forward, may further complicate matters since the rigid seat back may tend to increase the load placed on the already vulnerable seat mounting in front impacts.[9]

The Digitek Corporation carried out experimental crash studies in which a 1969 Beetle collided head-on into a full-size 1957 Ford.[10] Both cars were traveling at 30 mph. In the collision, the seat belt, the shoulder harness, and the seat-back locks failed on the VW. The Ford did not have a seat-back lock, but both the seat belts and the shoulder harness remained intact. The

Cornell Aeronautical Laboratory was soon thereafter commissioned by the Department of Transportation to determine if the restraint failures in the Volkswagen involved violations of the Federal Motor Vehicle Safety Standards.[11]

The conclusion of the Cornell study was that:

> Restraint systems . . . and front seat-back latches from the 1969 Volkswagen 1500 sedans did not fail when tested in accordance with the static load requirements of Federal Motor Vehicle Safety Standards No. 209 . . . and No. 207. . . .[12]

The fact that the seat complied with the applicable standard is in large part a reflection on the absurdity of the standard itself, a point discussed later in this chapter. One weakness of the standard is its failure to require a dynamic test, one in which the vehicle is actually crashed, to simulate collision conditions much more closely. The static testing specified in the standard involves simply subjecting the seat to loads from various directions while it is sitting still. Such a test is much less stringent than a dynamic test with the same load requirements. When the seats in question were tested dynamically, failure did occur at the equivalent of a 37-mph barrier crash for the VW.

Evidence of weakness in Volkswagen seats is not limited to research studies. Following the publication in a nationally syndicated newspaper column of the initial indications of a problem with VW seats, the Center for Auto Safety received numerous reports of VW seat failure.[13] Many were from attorneys concerning severe head injuries to front-seat occupants of VWs which were rear-ended. In Indiana, a 1969 Beetle driven by a young mother was hit from behind. Her seat ripped loose. She was found with her head rammed through the rear window. She survived the crash but died fourteen days later of brain injuries. In January, 1971, a husband and wife driving their 1965 Beetle on a state highway in Florida were struck from behind by a panel truck traveling at a higher rate of speed. Both front seats tore loose. The husband, who was at the wheel, was killed, and his wife's back was broken. Neither was thrown from the vehicle. In Sierra Madre, California, a 25-year-old driver of a 1967 Beetle stopped at a stop sign was rear-ended by a 1966 Ford traveling at 35 mph or less. The VW driver's neck was broken when it struck the rear window and window frame, after the seat separated from the track. The driver is now a quadriplegic.

Volkswagen seats, for two reasons, are less safe than the seats of the larger domestic cars and will continue to be so unless the Beetle is redesigned. This pair of factors is operative regardless of the fact that all seats, including those of the VW, may comply fully with the current standards of the federal government. First, the VW has a stiff rear-end structure primarily due to the location of the engine in the rear. If the car is hit from behind, this structure will not absorb energy gradually, as a more collapsible structure would. On this problem, D. M. Severy, one of the Institute of Transport and Traffic Engineering advisors on the UCLA crash study, has said:

> Stiffer rear-end structures will develop higher acceleration values for a given speed of impact and may require correspondingly stiffer seat backs having yield strengths at higher values, if comparable protection is to be offered.[14]

In other words, if the VW seat were to be made as *safe* as the seat on a domestic car, it would have to be made much *stronger*. (It should be noted that Mr. Severy has never published the results of any testing of VW seats—the UCLA study involved him only as an instructor. However, his conclusions about seating systems *in general* can be used to assess Volkswagen seats.)

Second, the relatively small size and weight of the VW means that if it is hit from the rear it will be knocked forward far more forcefully than a large car. The rate of acceleration is, in fact, inversely proportional to the mass of an object in a collision. Thus the VW's higher acceleration rate means that the forces on the seat will be both more sudden and of greater magnitude. This was graphically demonstrated in the UCLA crash test in that the Ford, which was about twice the mass of the VW, had acceleration rates only about half those of the VW. In a crash, the forces on the occupants are proportional to the rate of acceleration of the car. As the students said in their report:

> Laws of physics and the mass differential between most domestic vehicles and smaller cars imply that small cars must have proportionately stronger seats determined by their lower mass. If this is done, the smaller car would be made safer.[15]

It is worth noting in this regard that, while the VW seat must be stronger than that of a full-sized car if it is to be as safe, the VW's one putative advantage over a big car—its supposed maneuverability—does not come to VW's rescue. As the UCLA students noted in the conclusions to their report, "There is, however, one accident situation in which agility and maneuverability are of no use—being struck from the rear, especially by a larger car." [16]

In its defense VW has often argued that the present non-rigid seat is a positive safety factor, because, in yielding, the seat attenuates the forces causing whiplash injury. Even if this argument were valid, all cars manufactured after January 1, 1969 are required to have head restraints to prevent whiplash, so there is no reason that the seats on these vehicles should not be sufficiently strong to remain essentially rigid in a collision. Second, if non-rigid seats are to be offered as a positive safety factor, they should yield in a *controlled* manner, thus absorbing energy more safely, rather than suddenly, as they do now.[17] Also, the fate of the rear-seat passengers after the collapse must be seriously considered. As the UCLA crash test showed, a front-seat passenger could collide with the chest of a rear-seat passenger with sufficient force to injure both of them seriously. And finally it appears that in the Beetle, when the front seats collapse, the passengers are far worse off than they would have been had they only suffered whiplash. In many of the cases summarized in Appendix VII, the victims of rear-end collisions suffered severe head injuries from ejection or as a result of their second collision with the rear window frame. In sum, it seems obvious that if we are to be concerned with protecting passengers from whiplash, head restraints are a far better method than collapsing seats, and that given the seriousness of injuries resulting from failures of non-rigid seats, it is obvious that rigid seats are preferable to non-rigid seats.

It was previously noted that these dangerous seats meet the current federal safety standards relating to seats. That fact alone is an index of the standards' inadequacy. The federal standards for seat tracks were set in 1967, and have not been substantially changed since. The standard is even less stringent than was originally proposed since the original standard could not be met by manufacturer's products without modifications (see Appendix VII). The government bowed to industry pressure, but officially stated the reason for weakening the standard as follows:

> The proper anchorage of seats, however, was too critical to safety performance to remain uncovered by a safety standard while awaiting the completion of needed research that would yield more precise criteria than are presently available. The agency accordingly substituted, for the unproven load values as proposed, the set of load requirements which essentially conform with the GSA and SAE standards.[18]

A good deal of research has been completed on the effects of front- and rear-end collisions on seats. For example, D. M. Severy, formerly at UCLA's Institute of Transportation and Traffic Engineering, and his associates conducted a series of tests on occupant dynamics and seat design in relation to rear-end collisions beginning in 1954. Their recommendations as to seat anchorage and seat-back strength have varied somewhat over the years, but they have always been from five to thirty times stronger than the requirements of Federal Motor Vehicle Safety Standard No. 207 on seat strength.[19]

In a 1967 article, "Collision Performance, L[iberty] M[utual] Safety Car,"[20] Severy and others concluded that an integrated seat should have these specifications: with a 5000-lb. rearward force, the *seat anchorage* should not yield appreciably, and there should be a total deflection of the seat of no more than 4 inches measured at a point 14 inches above the "seating reference point" (the junction of the surfaces of the seat cushion and seat back). In addition, the *seat back* should be able to withstand a force of 5000 lbs. with no more than a 2-inch deflection at a point 14 inches above the seating reference point.[21] By contrast, requirements of FMVSS 207 are that the seat withstand a total load equal to twenty times its own weight (about 650 lbs. for the Beetle) and a torque about the seating reference point on the seat back of only 275 foot-pounds.* This is the equivalent of a force of 165 pounds applied to the seat back at a distance of 20 inches above the seating reference point. In testimony before the U.S. Senate Commerce Committee on March 20, 1971, William Stieglitz, former director of the Motor Vehicle Safety Performance Service of the National Traffic Safety Agency, interpreted FMVSS 207 in these words:

> Standard 207, "Anchorage of Seats—Passenger Cars," is an example of a standard that was weakened to such an extent that it is of little, if any, real significance. . . . The standard says that in a crash the anchorage of the seat shall be able to resist 20 times the weight of the seat. This means that if the automobile had a 20-gravity crash, and the seat had nobody on it, in other words was empty, this guarantees that an empty seat won't tear loose from the automobile in a 20-gravity crash. That is all it says.
>
> There is no provision for any loads from the occupant, from the restraining harness, or anything else on the seat. All this standard says is that if there is nobody on the seat in a 20g crash, the seat will stay anchored. I don't believe this means very much.[22]

In "Backrest and Head Restraint Design for Rear-End Collision Protection" Severy recommends seat back strength of at least 1330 ft-lb. and seat assembly and anchorage strength that would prevent failure from collision accelerations less than 20g.[23] And most recently, in "Safer Seat Design," presented at the 13th Stapp Car Crash Conference, Severy and associates proposed even greater protection—a seat back capable of withstanding 8333 ft-lb. with a limit of 10 degrees rearward deflection.[24] This is a thirty-fold increase over the torque requirement of FMVSS 207. In contrast, FMVSS 207, by our calculations, is designed to prevent seat failures at speeds not much higher than parking-lot maneuvers (see Appendix VII).

* Torque is an indication of twisting force about a point and is calculated by multiplying the force times the distance, from that point, of the application of the force.

Tests by Severy and others indicate that the federal standards for seat anchorage and strength are most inadequate. It is not surprising that only 41 compliance tests have been ordered by the NHTSA: 38 in fiscal year 1968, 3 in 1969, and none since. When asked why so few tests had been carried out, an NHTSA official said that the standard was so weak that compliance tests were meaningless. Thus, while VW argues that their seats meet federal standards, those standards guarantee next to nothing.

The seating system of a car (track, runners, seat back, and head restraint) is intended to provide safe restraint of the occupants of the car. The seat is as important in a rear-end collision as the seat belt and shoulder harness are in a frontal impact. Data show that VW seats do not provide the requisite degree of safety and restraint for the occupants of the car. The defect in the attachment of the seat runner to the seat track, compounded by the defect in the seat-back design, make the Volkswagen a most dangerous car in a rear impact. The studies indicate that the changes made over the years in the VW seat assembly have not significantly reduced the incidence of injury and death attributable to the seat failures, while the inadequacies of federal standards have complicated the issue by giving VW an undeserved patina of safety and by giving the company excuses to perpetuate its failures. Until VW ceases its rhetoric and corrects the seat-back and seat track defects—or until it is forced to correct them—the VW seat will continue to lead to maiming and killing.

## A Fair Weather Door Latch: Out the Door

Unlike many automobile crash victims, automobile safety myths die slowly. One lingering myth holds that, in a crash, it is better to be thrown clear of your automobile than to remain in it. A 1954 Cornell University Automotive Crash Injury Research (ACIR) report on occupant ejection injuries shattered that myth when it reported that ejection increased the occupant's risk of injury.[25] A later Cornell University ACIR study found that the risk of fatality was five times greater for ejected occupants than for non-ejected occupants.[26] Automobile safety researchers have also reported that occupant ejection is a leading cause of death in vehicle crashes and that a majority of the victims are thrown through opened doors.[27] Given such findings, the importance of strong door latch assemblies is obvious. This section will examine the performance of 1960–1971 Type I (Beetle) door latch assemblies when these cars crash.

The primary load that a door and its latch assembly must sustain is a force pushing inward or outward on the door; this is called *lateral loading* (Fig. 4), and it occurs in innumerable instances, from a passenger leaning casually against the door to the violent circumstances of

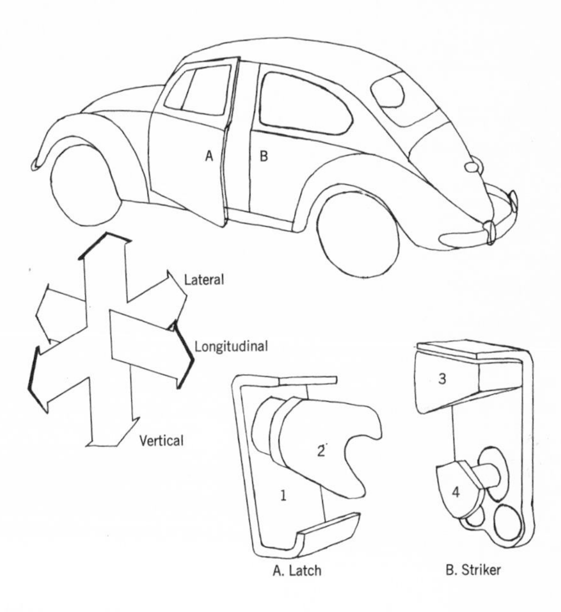


*Figure 4.* Door latch terminology. The latch assembly is a mechanical device designed to keep the vehicle door shut. Its basic parts are the latch (A), on the door, and the striker (B), on the door post. The plate (1) is a frame of the latch, and the rotor or bolt (2) is the part that engages with the striker. The wedge part of the striker (3) pushes down on the bolt to insure proper engagement between the latch and striker and at the same time serves as a vibration damper. The cap or plate (4) on the striker prevents the latch from disengaging from the striker during longitudinal loading of the latch assembly.

a side-impact crash. The idea, of course, is to keep the door shut. Several tests conducted for the National Highway Traffic Safety Administration (NHTSA) have demonstrated the weakness of the Volkswagen door when subjected to lateral loads. For example, in a National Bureau of Standards test of four different vehicles, including a 1965 Volkswagen Beetle, the VW door required the least amount of energy to crush the door (laterally) so that the inner door panel came within a foot of the center of the occupant seat, where it could cause injury. This indicates that the VW door itself offers less occupant protection than the doors on the other cars. During the same tests, moreover, the VW's door latch was the only one to disengage completely when the inner door panel collapsed to within a foot of the center of the seat—which indicates that the VW latch, too, is weaker than the latches on the other four cars.[28] In a test of five different vehicles conducted by the American Machine and Foundry Company for NHTSA, where the vehicle bodies were loaded with a longitudinal compressive load and the vehicle door was loaded with an inward lateral load, the 1968 VW sustained the only latch disengagements.[29] In addition, the door latch must take small vertical loads so that the door will be properly positioned and not rattle in its frame.

Until 1956, door latch assemblies on most cars were designed only for lateral and vertical loads. With the 1956 model year, American automobile manufacturers began to use interlocking latch assemblies which would resist loads in any direction. The importance of interlocking latch assemblies is that an interlocking latch is designed to remain firmly attached to the striker and thus will keep the door closed in a crash in which the door or door frame is distorted in such a way that the door latch would otherwise be pulled away from the striker. The loads for which the interlocking latch assembly is superior are longitudinal loads which pull the door frame backward away from the door; such load would separate an older type of door latch from its striker.

A study entitled *Test Procedures and Requirements for Door System Evaluation,* prepared for the NHTSA by Dayton T. Brown, Inc., confirmed that lateral inward loads placed upon a door induce longitudinal loads into the vehicle body.[30] Thus, any side impact on a car, whether by another car or from the car itself rolling over, is likely to allow a door to come open unless the door is equipped with an interlocking latch system. Furthermore, in a multiple impact situation, a latch partially damaged by the initial impact may fail completely during subsequent impacts, leading to possible occupant ejection.[31]

Although the need for interlocking door latches was recognized, and the technology for making them was available before 1955, Volkswagen waited until April of 1965 to act—ten years after the American car makers had put this inexpensive safety item on their cars. In the meantime, while many people were being killed and injured by ejections from Beetles,[32] three ACIR studies documented the effectiveness of the interlocking door latch assemblies.[33] The report of the most recent ACIR study (a contract report for the Department of Transportation) states:

> Among the pre-1956 models the percentage of cars that had one or both front doors opened in a rural, injury-producing accident was about 42 percent. Among the 1967–68 car models, the corresponding percentage was about 12 percent—a total reduction of approximately 70 percent in door opening frequency. . . .[34]

At present the best data on the frequency of doors opening in Volkswagen collisions are in the 1968 Cornell study on Volkswagen crashes reviewed in Chapter 1. Table I, taken from that report, shows (as would be expected) that the performance of the door latch assembly on pre-April 1965 VWs is comparable to other non-interlocking door latch assemblies, i.e., those used on pre-1956 American vehicles. A comparison of Volkswagen (60.5 percent) with post-1955 light American vehicles (38.1 percent), based on the percentage of vehicles with one or both front doors opened in principal rollover crashes, shows the advantage of interlocking door latch assemblies.

An open door in a crash is an easy avenue for occupant ejection, and the ejected occupant's risk of fatality

TABLE I [35]

Percentage of Cars with One or Both Front Doors Opened (Standardized by Impact Speed)

| *Car Group* | *Principal Rollover* * | *Collision* † | *Total* |
|---|---|---|---|
| Volkswagen | 60.5 | 29.8 | 35.6 |
| Renault | 52.2 | 36.2 | 38.5 |
| Foreign Sport | 34.2 | 26.6 | 26.5 |
| Corvair | 29.1 | 23.6 | 22.9 |
| Foreign Sedan | 59.5 | 25.4 | 35.4 |
| PRE 56 ‡ | | | |
| Light | — | — | — |
| Intermediate I | 64.2 | 38.9 | 44.2 |
| Standard | 69.2 | 37.4 | 43.2 |
| Intermediate II | 66.5 | 36.4 | 41.5 |
| Heavy | 66.0 | 28.6 | 37.0 |
| POST 55 | | | |
| Light | 38.1 | 25.3 | 27.7 |
| Intermediate I | 37.9 | 26.0 | 29.1 |
| Standard | 38.9 | 21.2 | 24.6 |
| Intermediate II | 46.9 | 23.7 | 28.3 |
| Heavy | 44.7 | 18.8 | 23.1 |

* Cornell defines a principal rollover (PRO) as ". . . an accident in which both collision and overturn of the car may occur, but major car damage is associated with the rollover." [36]

† Collision means any non-rollover vehicular impact with another object.

‡ Classes composed of American vehicles divided by vehicle weight. Only post-1955 American vehicle classes have interlocking door latch assemblies.

is five times greater than that for non-ejected occupants. The 1968 Cornell ACIR VW study reports that ejection was the leading cause of death in Volkswagen crashes; approximately 40 percent of all Volkswagen fatalities resulted from occupant ejection.[37] In addition, the Cornell study states:

> The greater risk of ejection in principal rollover accidents shown in Table 3.6 [Table II of this chapter] is particularly important because of the high frequency of overturn accidents observed for Volkswagen. Over 40 percent of the Volkswagens and 55 percent of the Renaults in this study overturned and when they did, about one out of every four occupants was thrown from the car.[38]

Table II illustrates the value of interlocking latch assemblies in reducing markedly the ejection rate in

TABLE II [39]

Percentage Frequency of Occupant Ejection by Seated Position, Vehicle Group, and Occurrence of Rollover

| Car Group | Drivers | | Front Passengers | | Rear Passengers | | All Occupants | |
|---|---|---|---|---|---|---|---|---|
| | *Collision* | *PRO* | *Collision* | *PRO* | *Collision* | *PRO* | *Collision* | *PRO* |
| Volkswagen | 11.0 | 35.8 | 9.9 | 29.6 | 3.4 | 15.2 | 9.5 | 31.1 |
| Renault | 19.8 | 30.0 | 14.3 | 28.4 | 12.5 | 8.5 | 17.5 | 26.7 |
| Foreign Sports | 8.7 | 41.4 | 8.5 | 44.9 | – | – | 9.1 | 42.9 |
| Foreign Sedan | 9.5 | 27.4 | 9.1 | 21.0 | – | 16.1 | 7.6 | 24.0 |
| Corvair | 6.1 | 12.9 | 5.6 | 14.9 | 7.8 | 14.5 | 6.3 | 13.9 |
| PRE 56 | | | | | | | | |
| Light | 19.0 | 50.0 | 13.6 | 33.3 | – | – | 12.5 | 40.0 |
| Intermediate I | 11.7 | 34.5 | 11.6 | 31.5 | 5.9 | 14.2 | 10.6 | 29.6 |
| Standard | 10.3 | 34.7 | 11.6 | 32.9 | 7.2 | 17.5 | 10.2 | 30.6 |
| Intermediate II | 9.6 | 37.1 | 9.3 | 39.0 | 8.3 | 23.0 | 9.2 | 35.0 |
| Heavy | 8.7 | 29.7 | 10.4 | 31.2 | 4.9 | 35.3 | 8.5 | 31.4 |
| POST 55 | | | | | | | | |
| Light | 5.7 | 20.0 | 7.0 | 21.3 | 3.8 | 4.8 | 5.8 | 17.7 |
| Intermediate I | 6.8 | 26.8 | 6.5 | 23.3 | 3.2 | 14.0 | 6.0 | 23.5 |
| Standard | 5.2 | 22.5 | 5.6 | 20.7 | 2.9 | 15.1 | 4.8 | 20.6 |
| Intermediate II | 6.0 | 27.3 | 6.3 | 25.0 | 5.1 | 11.8 | 5.9 | 23.8 |
| Heavy | 4.5 | 20.5 | 5.9 | 20.3 | 5.3 | 19.4 | 5.1 | 20.3 |

crashes. For example, 31.1 percent of all Volkswagen occupants were ejected in principal rollover (PRO) crashes studied, as compared to 17.7 percent of all occupants of post-1955 light American vehicles in PRO crashes.

But even before the importance of interlocking latch assemblies was proven statistically, their value was known. Automotive engineers were aware that they would provide a significant improvement in the safety of the door system as early as the late 1940s. In fact, Mercedes-Benz, another German auto manufacturer, touted its "safety cone" interlocking door latch when it was introduced in the early 1950s. Volkswagen did nothing.

For the 1960 model year Beetle, Volkswagen slightly modified the previous design of its door latch assembly by adding a raised lip to the top of the striker (Fig. 5). The only apparent purpose for this lip is to engage a locking plate, which would be mounted on the door above the latch, when the door is closed. The result would have been an interlocking latch assembly. Yet inexplicably Volkswagen waited until April 1965 to add the locking plate to the Beetle door. Volkswagen could have installed an interlocking door latch assembly at

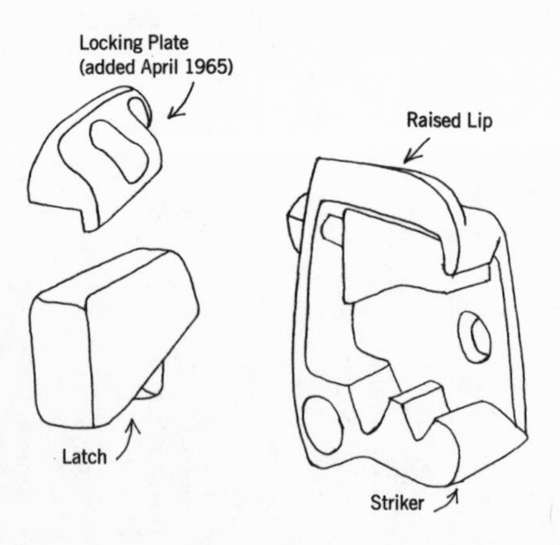


*Figure 5.* Pre-1967 VW latch assembly. Note raised lip which engages locking plate. Locking plate added April 1965.

least as early as the 1960 model year, if it had added the locking plate, a 35¢ dealer list price part.

Yet even if it had done so, it is unlikely that a significant reduction in occupant ejection would have resulted, based on the available evidence. Although there were few Volkswagens in the Cornell ACIR study with interlocking door latch assemblies of the type shown in Figure 5, Cornell did provide a separate set of statistics on about 1000 Volkswagens, 98 of which had the pre-1967 interlocking latch assemblies. Based on the limited data presented in Table III, the effectiveness of the VW interlocking assembly is not equal to its American counterpart. The reduction in door openings is only about 25 percent overall, from 43.4 percent to 33.7 percent; this compares to a 70 percent reduction in door opening frequency for U.S. models since the introduction of interlocking latch assemblies.

TABLE III [40]
Percent of Volkswagens with One or Both Doors Opened

| *Accident Type* | *Models without Safety Latch* | *Models with Safety Latch* * | *P* ** |
|---|---|---|---|
| Principal Rollover | 64.2% | 48.8% | >.05 |
| Without Collision | 61.9 | 51.5 | >.05 |
| Other PRO | 69.4 | 40.0 | >.05 |
| All Collisions | 28.4 | 21.8 | >.05 |
| *Total* | 43.4 | 33.7 | >.05 |

* Safety door latches introduced in models produced after April, 1965.

** P is a statistical symbol for the probability that a difference at least as large as that observed in the data would occur at random. If P is small, the data can be taken to be statistically significant.

With the 1967 model year Beetle, Volkswagen introduced a new interlocking system. The new latch has a bolt which rotates and hooks over the striker. The striker has a cap on its end which is supposed to keep the latch bolt from pulling away under longitudinal loads (Fig. 6).

Tests performed by the American Machine and Foundry Company for the NHTSA raised serious questions about the effectiveness of the latest of the Beetle door latch assemblies. AMF's contract called for tests of five different vehicle latch assemblies, including one from a 1968 Beetle. These tests were carried out in accordance with the requirements of Federal Motor Ve-

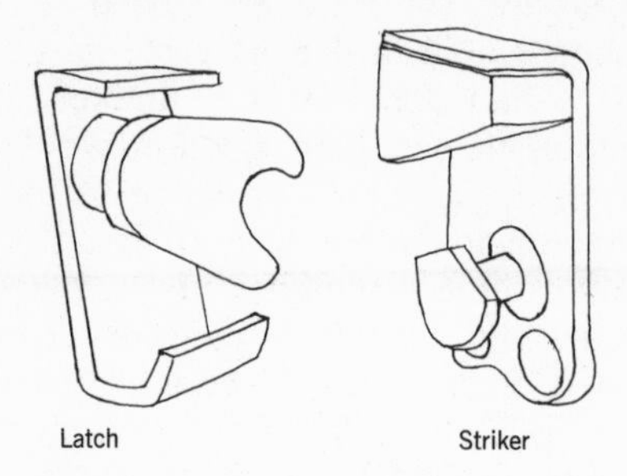


*Figure 6.* Post-1966 VW latch assembly.

hicle Safety Standard 206, which states that a door latch assembly must withstand a longitudinal load of 2500 pounds. Of the five vehicles tested, the only failure was the Volkswagen.[41] The VW latch failed at 2175 pounds when the latch bolt separated from its shaft.[42] This type of failure would allow the door to open under moderate longitudinal force. Although the AMF report was issued in July 1969, NHTSA has yet to conduct an official compliance test of the Volkswagen door latch assembly. Moreover, it will be at least fiscal year 1972 before a compliance test may be conducted on the VW latch assembly and sanctions imposed, if necessary.[43]

The failure of the VW latch assembly is inexcusable given the weak requirements of standard 206. This standard was written so that it merely endorsed the American automobile industry's own standard of the mid-1960s. For example, General Motors provided evidence to a congressional committee that the requirements of the standard (which went into effect on January 1, 1968) were first met by 1964 General Motors "A" line cars (Pontiac Tempest, LeMans, and GTO; Oldsmobile Cutlass and F-85; Buick Special and Skylark) and Chevrolet vehicles, and that all 1966 model year GM vehicles met the door latch standard requirements.[44] The standard obviously needs to be much stronger, since the latest ACIR study on door openings shows that doors on late model cars which meet this standard can still come open in crashes of moderate severity.[45] One defect of the standard is that it requires strength only in the latch itself and makes no mention of the strength of the mounting of the latch. Thus, although a latch may hold, its surrounding sheet metal may tear, allowing the door to open. What is needed, of course, is a standard which will test the performance of the door—frame, hinges, and latches—as a unit. In any event, the standard should be strict enough to ensure that door opening occurs in no more than one or two percent of all crashes. According to the Cornell study, door opening occurs in more than 20 percent of all crashes, even for the best groups in the study (see Table I).

Volkswagen of America continues to insist that no defects exist in its door latch assemblies. Early in 1971, in its house organ, *VW Dealer and Industry News,* VWoA asserted:

> Like the domestic industry, we have safety door latches which keep the doors from opening in an impact. There's nothing secret about that—look at the VW latches, the rigged elements interlock as on all U.S. cars. *We have gone even further.* Our exterior door handles have protected triggers to prevent unlatching in an accident. Our inside handles are also recessed to prevent them from being inadvertently released. *Our doors are safe. They meet all standards both for latches and hinges* [emphasis in original].[46]

The company's claims to its dealers cannot stand against the evidence of failure for both VW interlocking latch assemblies. The claims serve only to emphasize the question: Why was Volkswagen so tardy in adopting the interlocking latch assembly, and when it finally did so, why did Volkswagen use such poor quality devices? The design of an interlocking door latch assembly hardly presents a sizable challenge. Volkswagen of Germany applied in 1952 for a German patent on a motor vehicle door latch assembly with an interlocking feature (Fig. 7). The patent description of the assembly states in part, "Compared to known door latches, the invention distinguishes itself by special simplicity of construction and economy of manufacture." [47]

Even if Volkswagen had not had its own patent, there were numerous American, French, British, and German patents in the early and mid-1950s from which to choose an interlocking door latch assembly.[48] Furthermore, the interlocking assembly used on the Type III 1500 series

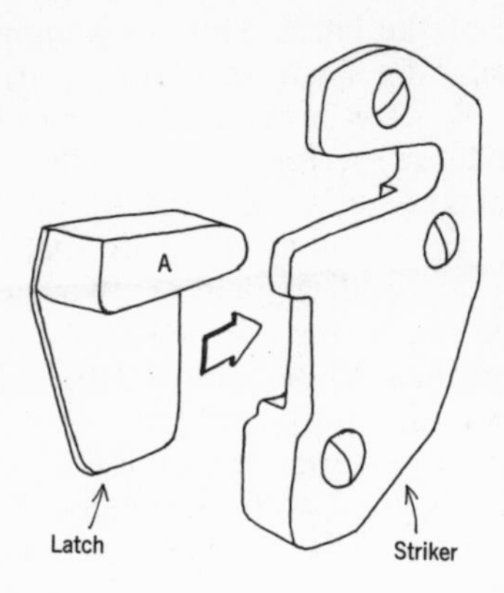


*Figure 7.* Illustration of latch assembly adapted from German patent 1,010,858. Surface A is attached to the edge of the door.

VWs, first introduced in Europe in April 1961 and imported into the United States in October 1965, was apparently the prototype for the latch introduced on 1967 Beetles (Fig. 8). With the addition of a larger cap to the shaft of the striker, VW could have introduced this interlocking assembly on the Beetle before 1967. One can only assume that Volkswagen had decided to take advantage of the lack of public concern for auto safety prior to 1966, by failing to install the interlocking assembly.

There is no question that the lives of the approximately 1.1 million owners of pre-April 1965 Beetles still

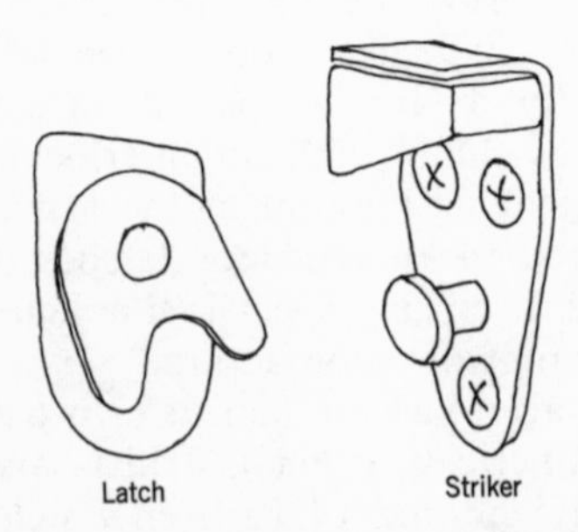


*Figure 8.* Latch assembly on 1961 Type III 1500 series VW.

in use [49] are unnecessarily endangered by the absence of interlocking door latches in their cars. Furthermore, the failure of the only VW latch tested under Federal Motor Vehicle Safety Standard 206, which went into effect with 1968 models, makes the safety of post-April 1965 door latches suspect. The standard is extremely weak; even proof of compliance will not establish the safety of the latch system. Until the standard is significantly upgraded and the VW latch is shown to meet the new standard, it is imperative for VW occupants to use belt and shoulder harnesses at all times to reduce the risk of ejection.

# 4

## *After the Crash: Up in Flames*

If the occupants of a VW involved in a crash remain in the vehicle and are not ejected through the rear window or out the doors, there are still other hazards with which to contend. One of the worst dangers is by fire. The performance of the Beetle's gasoline storage system is a serious threat to vehicle occupants in front-end crashes, which account for 60 to 65 percent of all Beetle crashes.[1]

The first problem with the fuel system is the location of the gas tank. All Beetles except the 1971 Super Beetle have the gasoline tank positioned immediately behind the spare tire (Figure 1). Only the bumper and the hood are in front of the spare tire, so that sufficiently severe frontal impacts can drive the spare tire, its wheel, and the sheet metal of the wheel well into the gasoline tank. These forces tend to reduce the volume of the tank, building up pressure inside it. Since gasoline is effectively incompressible, a tank which is fairly full will build up sufficient pressure so that the weakest part of the structure may yield. The integrity of the enclosure would then be destroyed, allowing gasoline to be released into the luggage compartment or to flow onto the pavement.

Even if the increased pressure is not sufficient to burst the tank, external forces, if sufficiently concentrated, can rupture it. For example, in July 1969 the gas tank

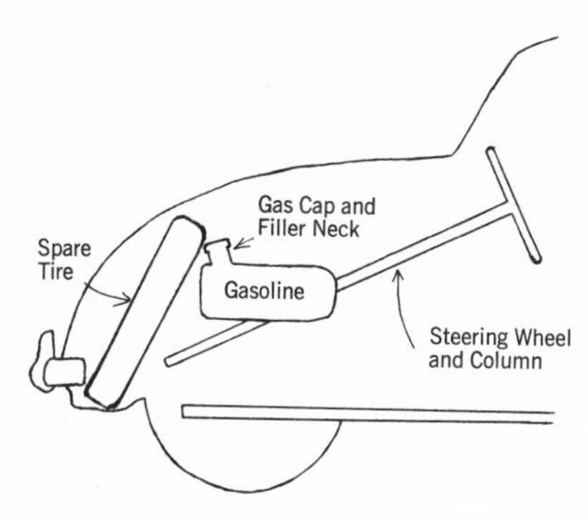


*Figure 1.* Gas tank location (all Beetles except Super Beetle). Filler neck location shown above is for 1961–1967 models.

of a Beetle being crash-tested by the National Highway Traffic Safety Administration was punctured by the jack mounting bracket which is located adjacent to the gas tank. Further, pressure can cause failure of the filler neck (where gas enters the tank) or of the fuel line connection (where it exits); in either case, gas can spill into the trunk and perhaps the passenger compartment. The fuel lines of a VW Fastback were sheared in a NHTSA crash test in May 1970. The NHTSA's only response to both this and the gas tank failure above was to write gentle letters to VW suggesting that they fix these hazards in future VWs (see Appendix V).[2,3] VW was not threatened with a stronger response, and no action was taken on behalf of present VW owners.

The Beetle gas tank is particularly vulnerable because the body of the tank is above the chassis of the vehicle including the frame head, the side rails of the frame, and the corrugated floor of the body (Figure 2). Thus in a collision with a vehicle with a higher bumper or frame, such as a truck or large car, the Beetle's fuel tank poses an extreme hazard as the other vehicle can easily crush the VW's front hood. Moreover, the tank extends down through a cut-out in the sheet metal floor of the luggage compartment, so that deformation of this part of the body will deform and possibly crush or rupture the tank. Even the fuel tank in a Corvair is entirely below

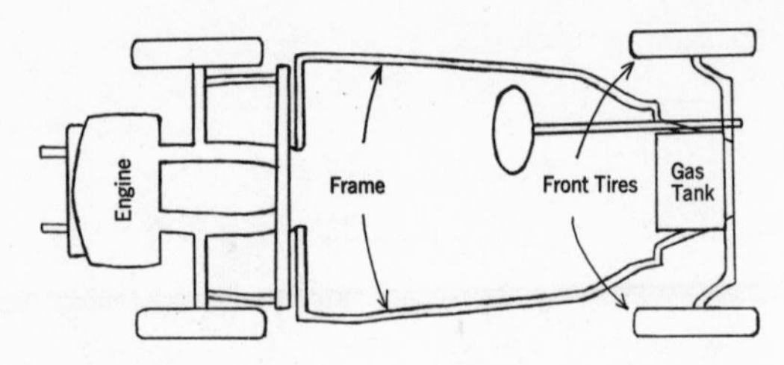


*Figure 2.* Gas tank location with respect to frame (Super Beetle excepted). Note extreme front location.

the floor of the luggage compartment, so that it is protected by basic structure against direct impact.[4]

Once the fuel system's integrity is destroyed—by tank rupture, gas cap dislodgment, or fuel line separation—gasoline will spill and can be ignited by sparks from the partially exposed electrical connections behind the instrument panel in the luggage compartment. Holes built into the Beetle firewall, to permit passage for wiring, the steering column, fuel gauge, and so on, can also provide passageways into the passenger compartment for flames and gasoline. The glove compartment, which projects into the trunk, and the cover over the back of the instrument panel are made from inflammable paperboard, providing an additional path for fire.

The second design factor which creates a further hazard is the way the fuel tank is attached to the car. American cars have steel straps to hold the tank securely in place, but VW uses four clips, which press down on the edges of the tank near the four corners. Volkswagen could have easily used the straps from the beginning, using the same bolt holes now used for the four clips.* (The Porsche 914, made by VW, uses a metal strap.) The problem with the four-point attachment is its rigidity; the tank acts as a structural member of the floor to which it is attached. In a crash, the floor can be pushed into the fuel tank as the whole structure crushes, thus distorting or rupturing the tank. Straps transmit less distorting force.

The third factor which weakens the VW's gasoline storage system (on 1961–67 models) is the location of

* And the company should recall Beetles to make the change (see Chapter 7).

the filler neck on the left front corner of the tank, immediately behind the spare tire. A frontal impact, particularly on the left front of the car, can shear off the filler neck, which protrudes about four inches above the top of the tank. Figure 1 illustrates the potential for contact between the filler neck and the spare tire, hood, edge of the luggage compartment structure, and fender sheet metal. In a front impact the rapid deceleration of the Beetle causes the fuel in the tank to surge forward, flow up the filler neck at the front end of the tank, and ram into the gas cap. The resultant forces can dislodge the cap, rupture the filler neck, or force the fuel lines off their connections at the bottom of the tank. Any one of these fuel system failures provides a convenient path for fuel spillage. (In the 1968 Beetle the fuel tank system was redesigned to comply with Federal Motor Vehicle Safety Standard 301. The filler neck was relocated and the gas cap redesigned. The neck now connects to the upper rear corner of the tank on the passenger side and runs up and out to the side of the car, where it is reached by opening an exterior cap.[5] Thus the location of the filler neck and gas cap is not a problem on new VWs, but approximately two million 1961–67 cars remain on the roads.)

The fourth, and perhaps most dangerous design defect of all, is the gasoline filler cap on 1961–67 models. These caps are so weak that they are easily dislodged in a collision in which the tank is slightly deformed. The propensity of the caps to become completely dislodged had been known to Volkswagen for two years before they were withdrawn from production and a sturdier cap was produced.[6]

Bertil Aldman, M.D., a Swedish crash-safety researcher, has also clearly documented this defect. The results of one of his frontal crash tests on the Beetle were reported in 1966 by the Official Swedish Council on Road Safety:

> Test No. 2 Impact velocity 14.7 m/sec [about 30 mph]
>
> Gas tank was filled to about 70 per cent of its capacity with water and standard gas cap was fitted in normal position. . . . Gas cap was found on the floor

after impact and a quite substantial amount of water had been spilled out during impact. . . . Gas tank was deformed by rearwards displacement of the spare tyre but showed no rupture. . . . The high speed film shows quite clearly that the gas cap jumps off at an early stage of impact and, starting at about 40 msec [milliseconds] after impact, a jet of water from the filler pipe is visible for about 450 msec.[7]

Based on the results of his tests, Dr. Aldman recommended that VW use a filler cap with threads which screw on to the filler neck, rather than the spring type engagement design then in production. Volkswagen, faced with the public disclosure of what they had discovered in their own tests, designed a new filler cap. The new design was a strikingly simple reinforced version of the spring cap (Figure 3). AB Scania Vabis, the Swedish VW distributor, then offered this new cap at company expense to all 250,000 owners of 1961–1967 Beetles in Sweden.

In the United States, the National Highway Safety Bureau (now the National Highway Traffic Safety Administration) under Dr. William Haddon began to study the problem in August 1968. But the engineering staff never became interested in this project, refused to assign an investigation number to the study, and, more importantly, insisted on limiting its scope to an analysis

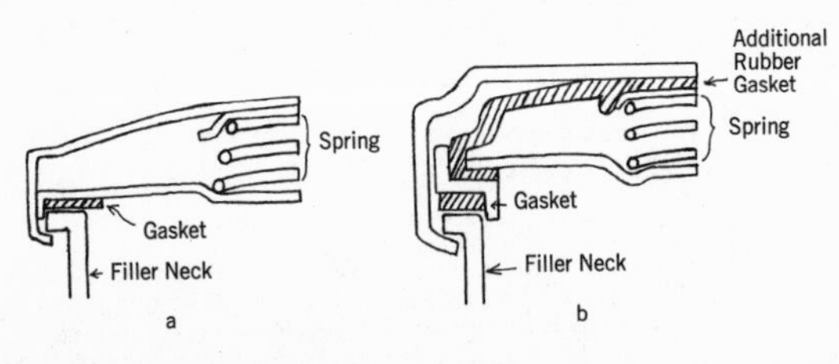


*Figure 3.* Cross sections of Beetle fuel caps: (a) fuel cap installed on 1961–1967 Beetles; (b) replacement cap manufactured to interchange with original on 1961–1967 models. Notice improved sealing and venting system and the thicker, stronger case in (b). The major improvement is extension and strengthening of the three protrusions that secure the cap to the filler neck.

of existing information on the frequency of VW fire crashes. No testing for gas cap dislodgment was ever conducted and VW was not even asked to submit information about its testing until nine months after the project got underway. Based on a superficial review of the few existing reports on fire crashes which contained information about VWs and other cars, the agency closed the investigation in March 1970 with no action.

VWoA, contradicting its Swedish counterpart, simultaneously denied that the 1961–1967 gas filler cap is defective and refused to alert owners voluntarily and to provide them with a new cap, stating that its authorized dealers stocked only the improved cap in the U.S. and that owners could buy it at a retail price of $1.95 (the current price is $2.10). Beetles sold in the U.S. with the model year designation 1968 and later have a new type of cap, in addition to the relocated filler neck described above. (In contrast to its lack of concern about the owners of the older models, VWoA in September 1970 recalled 4,900 of the 1971 Super Beetles for replacement of the gas tank filler cap which it said did not seal properly in the filler neck.)

A second Swedish study published in 1968 after AB Scania Vabis had decided to replace the hazardous caps for all owners of 1961–1967 Volkswagen Beetles in Sweden was highly critical of the easily dislodged gas cap. Bengt Pontén of the Department of Plastic Surgery, University of Uppsala, Sweden, also developed revealing findings on the question of fuel tank location in a study of 94 fire crashes in Sweden which resulted in 72 burn victims of whom 38 died, 23 sustained serious to moderate burns, and 11 escaped with minor burns.* Dr. Pontén's findings emphasized that the location of the gas tank is critical:

> Excluding the fires from reserve tanks it is found that front tank cars are responsible for 80% of the burns and 88% of the fatal burns in these cases.[8]

* Since neither the insurance companies nor the traffic authorities in Sweden registered fire crashes separately, Dr. Pontén uncovered these fires by reference to newspaper reports. The details were then verified with the aid of police, fire department, and hospital records. See Appendix VIII.

This high percentage is made more startling by the fact that cars with fuel tanks in the front (such as the Beetle) constituted only 20 percent of the vehicles in Sweden at the time of the study.

Pontén also commented on the design of the Volkswagen. He concluded:

> The fact that the tank cap is so easily dislodged might explain the seriousness of some of the fires, although the risk of damage to the tank itself still remains [even after distribution of new caps to Sweden's VW owners].[9]

In yet another study of the gas cap defect, the Digitek Corporation corroborated Dr. Aldman's observation. In a report entitled *Comparative Crash Survivability Program, Phase I Report,* Digitek described the result of a head-on collision of two Beetles (a 1969 and a 1961 model) each traveling at about 30 mph:

> On one vehicle [the 1961 model], the fuel tank filler cap was forced off the filler tube neck, permitting the filled tank to expel approximately three gallons of fluid into the front luggage compartment. The tank was slightly deformed, but did not suffer actual rupture of the tank itself or of the associated fittings (except for the filler cap). . . .
>
> The potential hazard associated with this fluid loss is judged high. The front end of the vehicle was deformed as was the wiring for the front end lighting. The possibility of a spark formed by a grounded headlamp wiring connection seems great. With an atmosphere of liquid and atomized fuel from the stream exuding from the filler neck, any spark would cause ignition of a fire in the immediate vicinity of the fuel tank.
>
> . . . the fact that one vehicle lost the filler cap is not excusable. The cap assembly should be designed in conjunction with the filler tube assembly such that some tank deformation is permissible without incurring either tank rupture or loss of the filler cap. This is practical, and within state-of-the-art design capabilities. . . .[10]

Studies by the Cornell Aeronautical Laboratory show additional evidence of filler caps becoming dislodged in collisions. A 1961 Beetle which was run at 30 mph into a vertical pole had significant gasoline spillage:

> High speed motion pictures show a moderate gush of dyed simulated fuel issuing from the right rear corner of the hood as it sprung open on impact. Dye stains showed that spillage extended about one quarter of the length of the right door, which opened fully and then closed again on impact, and down the side of the cowl at the right rear hood corner.
>
> The fuel spillage was estimated at less than one quart and was entirely due to gushing from the dislocated fuel filler cap which was located on the struck corner of the car. The tank was moderately distorted but did not display any leaks after the initial spillage was dissipated.[11]

A second VW test described in the same report gave similar results:

> Test number 8 was a 41.8 mph vehicle underride test of a 1966 VW. The barrier was elevated 18 [inches] above ground level. The front end, which houses the fuel tank . . . was completely collapsed. . . . Spillage occurred at an average rate of approximately 19 ounces by weight per minute over the first five minute period immediately following impact. The failure mode was a combination of gushing from the dislocated filler cap at impact and spillage through the fuel line discharge nipple at the tank bottom. . . . The tank was severely distorted . . . but did not split or suffer puncture.[12]

A contract report for the Department of Transportation showing fuel system inadequacies in the Beetle was prepared by the Fairchild-Hiller Corporation in 1969.[13] The report contains a section of post-crash studies where fire resulted from a crash. Case 6-1 is a crash in which a 1964 Beetle went into the rear of a garbage truck on a Long Island street. The crash was severe: the front of the VW was badly crushed. Two occupants died when the VW caught fire. Seven photos show, among other things, a dislocated fuel tank, a deformed filler neck, and a missing filler cap.

While VW is not the only vehicle with fuel system problems, as these reports show, VW does have a particularly serious hazard in the defective caps on 1961 to 1967 models.

In the summer of 1971 the Public Interest Research Group in Washington, D.C., was contacted with information about a deposition taken in February 1971 from Ulreich Seiffert, the Chief Test Engineer employed by Volkswagen, Germany, since 1966. In his deposition, Seiffert revealed that barrier crash tests of 1965 and 1966 Beetles had been performed by Volkswagen, Germany.[14] The filler caps came off in all tests just above 30 mph. These tests had taken place between September 1966 and October 1967. There was one test at 25.8 mph in which the cap did not come off, and five at between 30.6 and 32.6 mph in which all the caps came off.

In the summer of 1969 the National Highway Safety Bureau had asked VWoA for information about all laboratory tests related to the gas caps on 1961–67 models, but the Seiffert data had never been supplied. Although alerted to this new information and VWoA's withholding of it in violation of the law, the National Highway Traffic Safety Administration to date has refused to reconsider its earlier inadequate assessment of the issue.

The NHTSA's failure to find the gas cap defective was based primarily on two reports containing information about the overall VW fire crash rates in comparison to other vehicles. These reports—New York State Department of Motor Vehicles, *Volkswagen Fatal Fire Accidents, 1967* (released in August 1968), and Cornell Aeronautical Laboratory, *A Study of Volkswagen Accidents in the United States* (financed by Volkswagen of America and released in November 1968)—are frequently cited for the position that fires in Volkswagens are not a problem because they are not involved in a higher frequency of fire crashes than other passenger vehicles. For example, the New York study concludes:

> The data does [sic] not indicate that Volkswagens have a higher propensity of being involved in a fatal fire accident than other vehicles.[15]

Obviously not: the study doesn't even contain data for other vehicles! Contrary to what would be expected in a report with this conclusion, it contains data only for Volkswagens, thus precluding any independent analysis of the comparisons with other makes and models. The report, however, does contain the qualification that

> Additional data on fatal fire accidents in general is [sic] needed before a valid conclusion can be drawn. . . .[16]

This qualification generally has been ignored by those citing this report.

More importantly, the conclusion in the August 1968 report has been contradicted in a more thorough analysis of the same data released by the New York State Department of Motor Vehicles one month later, in September 1968. This report *does* contain data for other cars. Entitled *Fatal Non-Pedestrian Accidents Involving Fire by Make of Vehicle—1967,* the later report shows a Volkswagen fire rate of 2.34 percent. This is more than twice the rate for all other vehicles in the sample, which had a fire frequency rate of 1.11 percent.[17] Thus, the conclusion in the August 1968 report is misleading and incorrect. It should be repudiated by the New York State Department of Motor Vehicles.

The VW-financed Cornell report is similarly inaccurate in its conclusion that

> The frequency of occurrence of fire among Volkswagens involved in injury accidents was among the lowest observed in the data. Four of the 1130 Volkswagens (.4 percent) available for study burned.[18]

This statement cannot be directly challenged because Cornell fails to provide a rate for each make/model in the study. Instead, it has grouped other vehicles, precluding a make/model analysis. Indeed Cornell has refused to disclose data to individuals seeking to establish such make/model rates. The only other models which are given exact rates are the Renault (0.9 percent) and the Corvair (0.3 percent), both rear-engine vehicles with many of the same hazardous defects as the VW. Further, the study is broken into two classifications—

pre-1956 models and post-1955 models, with approximately the same number of vehicles in each. However, there are 24 pre-1956 VWs and 1106 post-1955 VWs in the study. As any statistician could point out, two such divergent distributions cannot be accurately compared in the same sample. Furthermore, since there were few pre-1956 vehicles on the road when this study was published in 1968, there was even less reason to include pre-1956 vehicles in a study of the comparative safety of vehicles in use—except, of course, to manipulate the study conclusions.

There were no fires in pre-1956 VWs in the study; the 0.4 percent fire crash frequency rate applies to post-1955 VWs. When compared to the other post-1955 vehicles in the Cornell study, VW has a higher, and hence worse, fire crash frequency rate than 56 percent of the other cars in the sample.

This Cornell study has been criticized by other sources as well. The University of Oklahoma Research Institute [19] has directly questioned the Cornell conclusions as to the number of vehicle fire crashes in the United States. It has also questioned the Cornell report's statistical procedures, such as not providing make/model data. A Scott Paper Company report listing information from randomly collected newspaper articles on car fires in 1968 contains modest probative material against the adequacy of the empirical base on which Cornell based its conclusion.[20] This study showed 18 VW fire crashes, for a frequency rate of 5.2 percent of the reported fire crashes where year and model identification were provided.

Evidence indicating the frequency of fire-related injuries and deaths in VW crashes is unfortunately sketchy and has been misrepresented in most of the reports published to date. However, it is difficult to dismiss the problem as inconsequential for several reasons: (1) Fire injuries, whether numerous or not, are usually serious and particularly painful, slow healing, and permanently scarring; (2) The assertion, if it were true, that the VW might not be much worse than other cars is really irrelevant if the fires are caused by defects; (3) Solutions to the problem are not complex, and in the case of the VW filler cap defect, easily and inexpensively remedied; (4) VWs tend to rollover, and according to a 1970 Cornell Aeronautical Laboratory report for the Department of Transportation, rollover in combination with fire "seems to produce a special hazard of its own due to the somewhat higher likelihood that the occupants will be trapped; inversion of the car or door jamming caused by roof deformation may make exit more difficult." [21] At present, the major danger in VW rollover crashes is ejection. But, as VW makes improvements in the retention capability of its windshield and in the strength of its door latches, the rate of entrapment may increase, making fire even more of a problem for the VW.

Among the improvements that could be made to the fuel storage systems of 1961–67 Beetles, most important is the replacement of the faulty cap with the redesigned cap available from VW dealers. Should this cap be purchased, the receipt for the purchase should be saved so that if VWoA is finally persuaded to conduct a recall campaign, the purchase price may be refunded.

Other changes which should be made are to place straps across the top of the tank so that the likelihood of the tank itself becoming dislodged in a collision is reduced. Another important change that should be made is replacement of the cover for the back of the instrument panel to effectively seal this area off from the luggage compartment with non-inflammable material. This would serve both to reduce the possibility of ignition from the wiring of the car, and to isolate the luggage space from the passenger compartment more effectively in the event a fire did start.

Since such a large percentage (62.3 percent in the Cornell study) of VWs involved in crashes experience the worst damage in the front area, a frontal collision in a Beetle poses a great danger of fire due to the front location and the poor design of the fuel system. As research reports on the various experimental safety vehicles show, an extreme front location (as the Beetle's) or an extreme rear location of the fuel tank would require a very sophisticated gas tank design (such as an aircraft self-sealing design) due to the increased vulnerability of these areas. It is obvious that Volkswagen will have to install a sophisticated fuel system or relocate the tank to a position less affected by crashes in order to meet the proposed safety standards for fuel system integrity; the latter would undoubtedly require a complete redesign of the Beetle in order to ensure compliance with the other proposed safety standards in such areas as handling, stability, and crashworthiness.

# 5

## *The VW Microbus: The Most Dangerous of Them All*

While the Type I VW is the most dangerous *car* in use in significant numbers in the United States today, extensive data indicate that the Type II (the "van" or "microbus") is by a wide margin the most dangerous four-wheel vehicle *of any type* designed for highway use and sold in significant numbers. This means that the microbus is more likely to take your life in a crash than any four-wheel vehicle you are likely to buy for driving on the public roads; figures cited in Chapter 1[1] indicate that drivers of microbuses are more than twice as likely to sustain serious or fatal injuries in a crash than drivers of the average car.

Several serious safety problems of the Type II were recently described in *Consumer Reports* (see August 1971 issue), which rated the VW bus as Not Acceptable. First, Consumers Union (CU) found the acceleration of the VW bus "so lethargic" that in their estimation it constitutes a safety hazard. Lack of power affects passing ability, uphill performance, and safety in merging onto turnpikes.[2]

The most serious safety problem in the microbus is the lack of occupant protection it offers in front-end crashes. Such protection can be provided by incorporation into the vehicle design of sufficient "crush distance," that is, the length of vehicle structure between the front crash surface and the front-seat occupant space. (Fig.

*Figure 1.* Comparison of crush distance in microbus and full-sized American car.

1). In a crash, this structure collapses and absorbs the forces generated by the crash. While most full-sized United States cars provide about three feet of collapse distance, the VW bus provides "a scant half foot." [3] Thus an unbelted front-seat occupant who is thrown forward in a crash can be directly involved in the primary collision between the vehicle and whatever it strikes. A severe crash may directly involve even a belted front-seat driver. In either case, excessive—even fatal—crash forces can reach the occupant.

Other bus wagons tested by CU are built with greater crush distance. The Chevrolet and Dodge vans each had more than a foot and a half of crush distance, and the Ford had about a foot. A VW spokesman, commenting in March 1970 on reports of lack of safety in VW vans, is reported to have said: ". . . in the Volkswagen bus, the driver sits at the extreme front of the vehicle . . . the injury rate [is] probably comparable to that of other vehicles with this feature." [4] This is hardly a reassuring statement. VW claims to have made safety improvements in the front-end design of the bus since the time of this statement, but nonetheless, in the view of CU, "half a foot of collapse distance is not enough." [5]

A third safety problem with the VW bus (and with other similar van configurations) is the failure of the steering column to provide energy-absorbing telescopic action the way it does in post-1967 cars. The nearly horizontal alignment of the steering wheel in a van reduces its potential for catching the driver as he pitches forward in a crash (slowing him down before he encounters other objects) to nearly zero. Instead, the driver, as he moves forward, hits the side of the steering wheel and thus the crash forces are concentrated on a small surface area.

Finally, the huge broadside area and relatively high center of gravity of the VW bus make it extremely sensitive to cross winds.[7] All vans have this problem (in fact, some roads and bridges are closed specifically to vans when the wind speed exceeds a specified limit), but the problem is more severe in VWs because of their lighter weight and rear engine. The VW van weighs in at 2904 lbs., a full 1400 pounds less than the lightest of the three domestic counterparts tested by Consumers Union. (CU's Dodge Sportsman weighed 4304 lbs.).[8]

It is one of many examples of the impotence of the federal rulemaking process that bus wagons and other "multipurpose vehicles" are exempted from many federal motor vehicle safety standards, notably those requiring head restraints, locking steering columns, and shoulder harnesses.[9] The VW does come equipped, however, with front-seat shoulder harnesses, but the absence of the others creates safety hazards in the bus; head restraints would reduce the incidence and severity of whiplash, and a locking steering column would reduce the incidence of collisions resulting from unauthorized use of the vehicle. Moreover, "forward control" vehicles,[10] including the VW van, are exempt from the far-reaching federal rule for passive restraint protection, (Standard 208 as revised), which will apply to most cars. This rule specifies that added crash protection, using some form of passive restraints, must be provided and tested in crashes up to 30 miles per hour. One example of a passive restraint is the air bag. Under present proposals, this standard would go into effect with 1976 models. But no such protection will be offered to occupants of vans, even through the 1978 models. The standard specifies only seat belts for "forward control" vehicles such as the van.[11] The safety standards are clearly deficient in this regard since front-seat occupants in vans are in a particularly dangerous position due to the lack of front crush distance. In evidence of the hazard, several law suits have been filed against VW for crash injuries sustained by front-seat occupants.[12]

It is important to note that the VW bus and the

Beetle share several of the defects discussed in other sections of the report, namely the suspension problems (rollover on pre-1969 models, and oversteer), lack of adequate crush distance, and the wheel rim deficiency.

In addition, the microbus and the Beetle have the same door latch assembly defects discussed in Chapter 3. The microbus also has a serious latch assembly hazard—the rear tailgate has a single stage rather than a double stage latch assembly. With a double stage assembly, there is both a primary and a secondary holding position of the latch or striker. Thus, when a door is not shut tightly, the secondary holding position still engages and the door will remain closed. On a single stage assembly, however, if the primary holding position does not engage when the door is closed, the door will open under slight pressure. Although Mr. Wolfhard Albers, a Volkswagen-trained engineer, has testified in court that a double stage latch assembly is a safety device used when passengers are anticipated to be in close proximity to a door, Volkswagen did not install such a latch assembly on any microbus rear door until the 1972 model year (after the initial release of this report). Astonishingly, the two-stage rear door latch on the 1972 can be retrofitted to the pre-1972 models.

The hazard of this defect is increased because the rear door may appear to be locked (the outside edge of the door may be flush with the door frame) when the latch has not engaged. Also, if a severe bump were to jar the latch assembly out of the primary position, the door would open. With a double stage assembly, the secondary position of the latch would prevent the door from opening. Therefore, a child riding in the rear of a microbus might be thrown against the door when the assembly is not completely closed and the door could open, allowing the child to fall onto the road. This could happen in traffic while the bus is still in motion.

This problem is particularly acute in the Volkswagen Campmobile, since there is a large, flat, cushioned space in the rear where a child might ride. Volkswagen's United States advertising has even pictured children riding in the rear of a moving Campmobile. This advertisement depicts two serious safety errors: the children are riding in a moving vehicle without restraint devices, and they are playing in supposed safety next to a door which does not have a double stage latch assembly. This particular ad further misleads parents by stating that the rear door has a safety latch.[13] Since Volkswagen has never informed microbus owners of this potentially fatal hazard, parents unknowingly allow children to ride in this area. Unfortunately, some of these children, like Lisa Gilmore of San Jose, California, have been severely injured when the rear door unexpectedly opened. Others have been killed. Volkswagen could easily have prevented such tragedies by installing an inexpensive double stage latch assembly.

# 6

## *Recalls, Defects, and Violations*

The National Traffic and Motor Vehicle Safety Act of 1966 makes it a violation of the Act, subject to penalties of $1000 per car with a $400,000 maximum, to sell any new vehicle in the United States if it does not meet the safety standards authorized by the Act. Since the passage of the Act, more than thirty safety standards have been issued. The initial group of twenty-one standards became effective on January 1, 1968—meaning, in effect, that cars had to comply at the beginning of the 1968 model year. Since then, the government has checked for compliance with the standards by conducting limited tests on various makes of cars. Based on the information released by the government through September 1, 1971, only twenty-five compliance tests have been conducted on Volkswagens, and they tested compliance with only ten of the standards. Among the critical safety items required by the standards but not tested even once on any VW models since the standards came into force are door latches (standard 206), head restraints (202), windshield glazing materials (205), and windshield retention (212). Of the twenty-five tests that were made, moreover, fourteen were failures, and several of the failures were critical.*

* By contrast, for all other cars there have been 2431 compliance tests, of which 185 were failures, a 7.6 percent failure rate.[1] VW's failure rate is 56 percent. (All figures as of January 1, 1972.)

From 1968 through 1971 models, about a million and a half Volkswagens were sold in this country. It is probable that many of them share the defects found by the compliance tests. These cars endanger the lives of their passengers. Yet every so-called government investigation of Volkswagen compliance test failures has been terminated without government action against Volkswagen. Even though the failures have been serious, the National Highway Traffic Safety Administration has closed its investigations by writing a mild letter to VWoA gently chiding the firm for its illegal and dangerous conduct—conduct that amounts to gross negligence—and requesting improvements in future models. (A chart of the failures and examples of several of the agency's letters are in Appendix V.)

In one compliance test failure, the 30-miles-per-hour barrier crash of the 1968 Type III Fastback, the two fuel lines at the lower surface of the fuel tank sheared off, causing excessive fuel leakage. The agency concluded that this failure did not violate the fuel tank integrity standard (301) and has refused to conduct an investigation until it receives more information about the problem. The agency's surrender was typically passive. Although it termed this performance a "marginal safety conditon,"[2] it did not alert the owners of these vehicles or issue a bulletin to all owners requesting more definitive information. Based on the meager information in the public investigation file, NHTSA did not conduct any further tests to determine how widespread the problem is and, astonishingly, it did not even require Volkswagen to submit information on its tests, warranty claims, or accident investigations.

Similarly, in the 30-miles-per-hour barrier crash of the 1969 Beetle, the fuel tank was punctured by the jack mounting bracket, causing excessive gasoline leakage. Although presumptively a violation of standard 301, the agency concluded: "Since only a few examples of fuel tank rupture by the assembly are presently known, a defect notification campaign is not considered necessary at this time." (See complete letter in Appendix V.) The agency asked VW to move the jack mounting bracket on future models, which VW did, beginning with the 1971 model. However, the agency took no further action; it did not require VW to notify owners of the dangers of the jack location, nor did it ask VW to recall the affected VWs to correct the problem.* Drivers and passengers in pre-1971 Beetles continue to be subjected to an unnecessary risk of fire if their cars crash.

The National Traffic and Motor Vehicle Safety Act also requires every manufacturer of vehicles sold in the United States to notify owners of safety-defective vehicles. VW has as a result recalled about ¾ million vehicles since enactment of the law in September 1966. During this same period, about 2½ million new VWs have been registered in the United States. Thus, about 30 percent of the new VWs sold during the last five years in the United States have been recalled.

Volkswagen Recall Campaigns and VW Vehicle Registrations in the United States by Model Year 1967–1971

| *Model Year* | *Vehicles Recalled* | *U.S. Registration of VW Vehicles* |
|---|---|---|
| 1967 | 90,147* | 456,231 |
| 1968 | 492,798 | 567,975 |
| 1969 | 40,217† | 540,623 |
| 1970 | 11,688 | 571,441 |
| 1971 | 111,276 | 511,395 |
| *Totals:* | 746,126 | 2,647,665 |

Sources: Vehicles Recalled: *Motor Vehicle Safety Defect Recall Campaigns,* from September 9, 1966 to December 31, 1971, published quarterly and annually by the National Highway Traffic Safety Administration, Department of Transportation, Washington, D.C., and sold by the United States Government Printing Office. Registrations: Volkswagen of America.

* Includes some 1966 models and 5,157 reported in 1967 with no model year designation.

† Includes some 1968 models.

Although VW has had so much practice conducting recall campaigns, the company still does not do an adequate job, according to a study by the Transportation Research Division of Intext for the U.S. Department of

* For owners wishing to do for themselves what VW should have done, correcting the defect is not difficult. Drill out the rivet which holds the jack mounting bracket to the wheel-well wall and remove the bracket. Move the whole assembly to a safe location, such as under the rear seat, by drilling a small hole in the surface on which the jack is to be mounted and securing the mounting clip with a bolt or sheet metal screw.

Transportation in May 1970.[3] This report reveals that of eight major foreign and domestic manufacturers whose recall campaigns were studied, radically fewer VW owners (60 percent compared to a study average of 86 percent) [4] ever received the legally mandatory notification letters. Also, 15 percent of the VW owners (compared to a study average of 8 percent) [5] stated that the defect in their car was not corrected. When asked whether they were satisfied with the manner in which their automobile recall was handled, 24 percent of the VW owners said "no," compared to a study average of 12 percent negative responses.[6] These comments by VW owners indicate extraordinarily inferior recall campaign performance by VW. Although applicable only to a 1968 campaign, these facts warrant further federal scrutiny to assure compliance with the law.

The completed defect investigations file at the Department of Transportation contains illuminating insights of Volkswagen's arrogant disregard for the reliability of its product.

For example, the Department of Transportation asked VW for information (IR 60) [7] about 1968 Beetle windshield wiper motor failures. In response VW admitted there had been 2,902 claims for repair or replacement of wiper motor armatures on 1968 Type I vehicles (Beetle and Karmann Ghia) during the first 10 months of 1968, but claimed that this was insignificant since it represented only 0.8 percent of the 363,045 Type I vehicles imported during this same period. Such a statement is obviously irrelevant since many of the potential failures on these vehicles had not yet had a chance to occur. Further, VW argued that warranty statistics must be viewed with caution because it is not possible to determine the extent to which they represent driver negligence rather than product failures. No explanation was provided on the obviously remote possibility of driver negligence causing wiper motor armature failure. Moreover, VW claimed that the motor failure was not a safety defect because the failure would be gradual, thus providing ample warning to the driver to get the motor replaced before total failure occurred. Although there is a Department of Transportation safety standard on vehicle windshield wiper performance, the agency accepted VW's explanation and closed the file.

Another VW safety defect was documented in the file on Information Request 61. This concerned horn failure on pre-1968 Type III models (Squarebacks and Fastbacks) caused, according to VW, by a chemical reaction inside the steering wheel horn assembly. The plastic used in this assembly would release ammonia when damp and this would cause corrosion of the electrical contacts and horn failure. Volkswagen admitted that 3,066 horns were repaired between August 1966 and October 1968 but stated that since 171,641 Type III vehicles had been imported during this same period, the failure rate was only 1.78 percent. This percentage is misleading, however, since many of the vehicles which had been imported in that period either had not been sold or had not been in use long enough to develop the problem. Also, the company argued that this was not a safety defect since the owner would recognize the change in horn tone before total failure occurred. This is little consolation for drivers without perfect pitch, or those who drive with enough consideration to use their horns infrequently, or for drivers in urban areas where street noise might mask the change in pitch, or for drivers—presumably a majority—who would not realize that a change in horn tone might be a prelude to horn failure. Nor does VW indicate the percentage of failure in humid climates, although the plastic is unlikely to get damp as often in, say, Phoenix as in New Orleans.

A recent VW safety defect in 1968 and 1969 Squarebacks and Fastbacks was highlighted by the Center for Auto Safety in an August 2, 1971 press release which described the reverse orientation of the louvers through which cooling air is drawn into the engine compartment. Many of these vehicles, but especially those with air conditioning and automatic stick shift, have experienced engine trouble due to overheating. This design mistake could lead to engine failures which might cause a serious crash.

A modification kit (VW Part Number 361 898 975, list price $10.30) was manufactured for the correction of this defect, and Volkswagen has provided a so-called goodwill or courtesy extension of the warranty to

36,000 miles for correction of the problem.[8] However, the owners of these vehicles have not been warned and unless they complain, they will not be aware of the availability of the free correction.

Arthur Railton, Vice President of VWoA, in his letter of August 10, 1971, to the Center claimed that the need for additional cooling air exists only in highly specialized circumstances, usually on vehicles equipped with a combination of air conditioning, fuel injection and automatic stick shift and operating "when the outside temperature and traffic conditions were on the extreme end of the scale." Explaining Volkswagen's policy on repair of the louvers, he said:

> . . . we developed a kit to increase the effective openings in the air intakes. We instructed our dealers to install these kits at our expense on those vehicles with this combination of factors and likely to be operated under the extreme conditions mentioned above. If the overheating is going to occur it will do so within the period covered by our reimbursement program. If certain exceptional circumstances cause it to occur after that period we judge each case individually and decide whether payment is warranted.

The Center responded on August 13 asking why owners themselves were not notified directly. It appears that dealers are not informing owners of VW's policy. Several owners said that they did not know about the defect until after their engines had been damaged by overheating.

The Center's letter to Railton also pointed out that VWs do not have temperature gauges. Thus it is difficult for the driver to monitor actual engine temperature while driving other than by vehicle malfunction. Thus an overheating problem which causes premature oil breakdown and associated engine wear—but not severe engine failure—would not be known or even apparent to the owner. Volkswagen has not yet responded to the Center's latest letter.

Volkswagen's advertising strategy gives the potential owner the impression that he will be dealing with a far more conscientious company if he purchases a VW. But Volkswagen is no longer the small struggling company which imports only a handful of vehicles; the corporation is now a giant conglomerate, ranking as the world's third largest auto manufacturer and the largest vehicle exporter. As the facts in this chapter show, Volkswagen's actions are in many respects much more reprehensible than those of the large American manufacturers. These actions include VW's basic scrimping on safety (which constitutes the defects), the high percentage (56 percent) of failure in compliance testing, the insistence that owners pay for such items as an improved replacement gas cap, and, even when VW initiates a recall campaign, its inexcusably poor performance in notifying owners and correcting the problem to the owners' satisfaction. Apparently VW's definition of a safety defect is very narrow, admitting only those deficiencies which are so severe that the company's legal liability would outweigh the cost of the recall campaign.

# 7

## *Conclusions and Recommendations*

The Volkswagen Beetle is the most hazardous car currently in use in significant numbers in the United States.[1] This conclusion is based on the following factors: the danger of injury from the windshield, the weakness of the seat tracks and seat backs, the likelihood of the doors opening in a crash, the consequent likelihood of passenger ejection, the dangerous location of the gasoline tank, the propensity of the gas cap and the gas lines to come off during a crash, steering-column penetration in a frontal crash, the vulnerability of the doors to side impact intrusion, extraordinary side-wind sensitivity, and handling qualities which make the car quite unpredictable. These factors not only give the Beetle a higher propensity toward involvement in single-vehicle crashes than most other cars, but also make the Beetle more likely to cause serious or fatal injury in any collision than virtually any other car in common use in this country.

While the worst Beetles are those produced before 1968, the partway measures in 1968 and later models have not been at all adequate to deal with the number and magnitude of the Beetle's safety hazards. Even the current Super Beetle suffers from important safety design lapses which show that VWAG has yet to become seriously concerned about the safety of the people who travel in Volkswagens.

While the Beetle is unsafe, there are measures which can be taken to diminish its worst safety deficiencies. On the other hand, the VW microbus or van is so unsafe that it should be removed from the roads entirely. The fundamental reason to avoid purchasing or riding in any microbus is the flagrant lack of front collapse distance even when compared to similar vans of other manufacturers. The changes which would be required to render the microbus acceptable for anything other than low-speed, off-road operation would probably cost more than the current value of these vehicles. The incredible disregard for safety exhibited by VW in designing even the current generation of microbuses, introduced in late 1967, is beyond comprehension.

Volkswagen's disregard for safety is all the more deplorable when one considers the fact that the technology for making it a safe car, as well as the general awareness of the need for designing safety into cars, has been known for some time. While there may have been some explanation for Dr. Porsche's oversights in the early 1930s, by the middle 1950s, when VWs first began to enter the U.S. in significant numbers, patents were available for such important safety features as safety rim wheels, interlocking door latches, and double-jointed rear axles. One can only conclude that the most important priority for VWAG was to make their cars as simple and profitable as possible. While Volkswagen may be lauded for avoiding the mania of the annual style change and in earlier years for providing vehicles with a good frequency of repair record, these positive factors hardly offset the critical hazards of the VW.

Volkswagen's reaction to safety criticism has been facile and self-serving. Little evidence is provided to back up the company's contention that the VW is a safe car. It further obfuscates the issue by claiming that the VW meets all applicable federal motor vehicle safety standards. This claim is irrelevant for several reasons. First, the federal safety standards do not cover such key areas of vehicle safety as handling or vehicle deformation in a crash. Second, as is well recognized, these standards are minimal and no claim is made that a complying car is crash survivable at any minimal speed. Furthermore, the company's claim may be false, since minimal government testing of VWs against these standards shows failures in 14 out of 25 tests, including failure of critical safety belt and gas tank integrity standards. Only the timidity of the government in not following up on these tests has let VW get away with the claim that its cars meet federal standards. Finally, VW lobbies the agency to keep federal safety standards at the lowest common denominator which VW represents. This position pleases both the State Department and United States manufacturers, particularly those who sell in West German markets and want to avoid retaliation.

The claim that the microbus meets the applicable motor vehicle safety standards is even more ludicrous since many of the important automobile standards do not apply to these and other forward-control vehicles. Even the claim that the VW is as safe as cars of similar size and weight (which has not been proved) misses the point that about half of all subcompact cars in use in the United States are Volkswagens. Thus their potential for injury and death is far greater than for any of the others.

The recommendations of this report deal with the following aspects of the Volkswagen problem:

A. Size as a safety factor
B. Responsibilities of Volkswagen
C. Responsibilites of the National Highway Traffic Safety Administration

A. *Size as a Safety Factor*

Small size and light weight impose inherent limitations on the degree of safety that can be built into a vehicle. All known studies relating car size to crash injury conclude that occupants of smaller cars run a higher risk of serious or fatal injury than occupants of larger cars.

In spite of this limitation, small cars can be substantially upgraded in their roadworthiness, or pre-crash behavior, and their crash survivability. Further, the economic use of natural resources in small cars and their greater convenience in urban settings may be sufficient reason to apply more safety in small cars. The primary considerations which must be made in the design of small cars are the following:

1. Lightweight cars are at a severe disadvantage in collisions with heavier vehicles. This is because in any collision the force of each vehicle on the other is equal, so that the lighter vehicle will sustain a higher rate of acceleration or deceleration. Thus the occupants of the lighter vehicle will be subjected to greater forces than the occupants of the heavier car. To compensate for this inherent disadvantage, small cars must be designed with adequate restraint devices. For a small car an adequate restraint system must distribute the greater forces over a large area, and be designed to encourage a high usage rate. Until such devices are incorporated, all passengers of small cars should be warned of this hazard and urged to use seat belts and shoulder harnesses.

2. Small exterior dimensions limit the amount of crush distance that can be built into small cars. Adequate crush distance is necessary for occupant protection because during a collision the occupant compartment must be decelerated as smoothly as possible to minimize passenger injury. With limited crush distance available in a small car, its crashworthiness is much more important than in a larger car.

3. Since interior space is limited in a small car, the importance of keeping this space intact in a crash is even greater than for a larger car. No intrusions either from its own components or from the impacting object should be permitted, since the distance between the walls of the car and its occupants is very short. The doors and windows must not open in a crash, but they must yield to occupant impact in such a way as to minimize injury (absorbing energy without causing lacerations); this means installing guard beams in the doors, improving the windows so they absorb more energy before rupturing, and reducing hostile projections (knobs, handles, unpadded areas) inside the car.

4. Handling must be predictable and the car must be reasonably stable, factors that do not generally inhere in small, lightweight cars. The ratio between the height of the center of gravity and the track width must be enough so that the car cannot be overturned easily. There is no inherent reason why a small car should be more sensitive to side winds than a large car. If achiev-

ing reasonably low levels of side-wind sensitivity cannot be accomplished in rear-engine designs, such designs should be abandoned.

If the current Volkswagens are assessed by these standards, it will be seen that they are woefully lacking in all categories.

B. *Responsibilities of Volkswagen*

It is indicative of Volkswagenwerk AG's indifference toward the safety of its vehicles that the company delayed incorporation of numerous known safety designs into its Beetle until after independent studies emphasized the need for them. Until about five years ago VWAG was so little appreciative of the need for safety designs that it did not have an identifiable engineering group whose primary mission was vehicle safety. Clearly, as the auto companies now recognize, this is an area for organization specialization within the corporation.

The investigation for this report leads to the conclusion that Volkswagen of America has an obligation to recall all Volkswagen vehicles for the safety defects listed below. Unfortunately many casualties and costs inflicted on VW owners and passengers in the past through callous vehicle design hazards cannot be recovered. But, at the very least, the correction of these deficiencies should be made at no cost to the owners of these cars.

1. Seat Track Weakness. The likelihood of seat track separation in Beetles produced before the 1971 models has been well documented. These tracks must be strengthened either by replacement or by some other means so that they will not separate when the car is rear-ended by a full-size car at only 30 mph. Seat tracks in 1971 Beetles and in other VWs should be tested to determine their adequacy.

2. Seat Back Weakness. The tendency of the seat back to collapse under moderate force loadings is due to the relatively thin gauge steel tubing used in this component. This frame should be replaced or strengthened consistent with the improved strength of the seat track suggested above. At the same time, head restraints, which conform with FMVSS 202, should be added to

the seats of Beetles produced before 1968. This is necessary so that the added strength of the seat will not cause equally serious whiplash injuries to the neck. Again, testing should be carried out to determine the adequacy of the seat backs in other Volkswagen models.

3. Door Latch Deficiencies. The question of compliance of the latest Beetle door latch must be settled immediately. If the latch does not comply, the 1967–71 cars equipped with this latch must be refitted with a latch which does meet the standard, and Volkswagen must be fined for non-compliance with this standard.

VW door latches used on vehicles manufactured prior to April 1965 cannot by definition meet any test standard since those latches were not of the interlocking design. VW could easily have made the 1960 and later model door latch assemblies interlock by adding a plate which would have interlocked with a striker lip that was introduced on the 1960 model. But the locking plate—for reasons best known only to Volkswagen—was omitted until April 1965. If this assembly is found adequate by testing against the Federal Motor Vehicle Safety Standard No. 206, the plate should be added to all 1960–65 models on which it is lacking. If not, an alternate door latch which does comply should be installed on 1960–66 Beetles. In either case, an adequate interlocking latch must also be installed on the doors of all pre-1960 Beetles still in operation.

4. Fuel System. Among the improvements that could be made to the fuel storage system of the 1961–67 Beetles, the most important is the replacement of the faulty fuel cap with the redesigned cap now available from VW dealers. The Swedish VW distributor, AB Scania Vabis, offered this cap free in 1968 for all 250,000 1961–67 VWs which were then in Sweden. VW should install straps across the top of the fuel tank to provide better anchorage. VW should produce a redesigned cover for the back of the instrument panel and supply it to owners at no expense. This cover should effectively seal this area, which houses electrical components, from the luggage compartment, where the fuel tank and filler neck are located. The material for this cover must be non-inflammable. Hose clamps should be installed on all flexible fuel lines. Crash testing must be

performed to determine if additional changes are needed in the Beetle's fuel system. Testing should focus on the vulnerability of the tank due to its proximity to the structural members of the vehicle, the necessity of sealing off passageways for fuel and fire into the occupant compartment, and the relocation of the jack assembly.

5. Wheel Rim Inadequacy. VW should produce a five-lug wheel with a safety rim and make it available, free of charge, to those owners of VWs produced prior to October 10, 1967. This rim would prevent airout and help to hold the tire carcass on the rim in the event of a blowout or puncture.

6. Seat Belts and Shoulder Harnesses. Volkswagen should retrofit seat belts and shoulder harnesses, free of charge, in all VWs presently lacking them. This is the minimum step which must be taken to reduce injuries due to lack of interior space.

7. Handling. In order to reduce the number of injuries and deaths due to the problems of Beetle handling, Volkswagen should:

(a) Encourage the use of and supply to the dealers five-inch wheel rims of the safety type. Wider tires mounted on such wheels would improve traction.

(b) Provide anti-roll bars for the 1959 and earlier models for installation on the front suspension.

(c) Undertake a massive advertising campaign to alert VW drivers to handling problems with the Beetle.

8. Future production model Volkswagens should incorporate all improvements listed in this section, as well as side guard door beams, additional front and rear crush space, and further improved suspension systems. Other problems such as the side-wind sensitivity and large center of gravity height to track ratio cannot be corrected in the current Beetle design. This design should be phased out as soon as possible. Volkswagen microbus production should cease immediately.

We estimate the cost of a recall campaign to make these corrections on all Beetles now in use to be approximately $184,000,000.[2] This total estimate is based on Table I which appears below.

The production costs of the replacement parts are estimated at about 40 percent of typical manufacturer sug-

TABLE I

Estimated Costs of Parts and Labor for VW Recall

| *RECALL ITEM:* | *Seat Track* | *Seat Back* | *Head Restraint (2/car)* | *Door Latch (2/car)* | *Fuel Cap (1/car)* | *Fuel Tank* | *Wheel Rim (5/car)* | *Seat Belts (4/car)* | *Shoulder Harness (2/car)* |
|---|---|---|---|---|---|---|---|---|---|
| Number of Cars Affected (in millions) | 3 | 3 | 2 | 3 | 2 | 3 | 2 | ½ | 2 |
| Approximate Production Costs of Parts (per car) | $1.00 | $1.00 | $10.00 | $0.30 | $1.00 | $2.00 | $25.00 | $9.00 | $7.00 |
| Approximate Cost of Labor (per car) | $4.00 | $4.00 | $5.00 | $1.70 | — | $2.00 | $10.00 | $5.00 | $4.00 |
| Total Cost of Recall Item (in $ millions) | $15 | $15 | $30 | $6 | $2 | $12 | $70 | $7 | $22 |

Estimated total costs of parts and labor for this recall campaign, based on the above figures, is $179,000,000.[2] The net expense to Volkswagen is, of course, much less after deductions and tax write-offs.

gested retail prices. Since there is no sale involved. price of the recall campaign is calculated at cost. Thus, neither the dealer nor VWAG would make any profit on the installations made.

For example, a replacement fuel cap, already in production, retails for $2.10. Volkswagen's cost to produce this part and ship it to the dealer is approximately $1.00. We do not list a labor charge for the improved fuel cap replacement since most VW service centers would install this item at no charge to the customer. On some items a design improvement is not already in production. In these cases the cost could be different than our estimate. For example, Volkswagen might decide to combine the improvements of the seat track, seat back, and head restraint and provide each owner with a totally redesigned seat and track system. This solution might be even better than separate retrofits for each problem but may be more expensive.

The figures for approximate cost of labor are based on a labor rate of $8.50 per hour. Added to the costs of parts and labor is $5 million for the expense of printing, national advertising, and mailing notifications of recall to 3 million owners (see Table I).

VW microbuses (Type II) still on the road should be removed from operation entirely. It would be much more expensive than the value of the vehicle to attempt to retrofit safety features to the bus. Even in the event that some improvements could be made and the problem of lack of crush distance alleviated, the Type II still would not meet minimal safety acceptance criterion due to its high center of gravity, its sensitivity in cross winds, and its inadequate power. Therefore, Volkswagenwerk AG should recall all Type II vehicles and reimburse each owner for the present retail value of his bus.

As a precondition to any future assertion by VWoA that the Beetle is a safe car, the company should make public the following information:

1. A full disclosure of all crash testing carried out by VWAG on their cars.
2. A full disclosure of all tests of the Volkswagen suspension system including all instances of rollover.
3. A summary of all investigations made into actual

vehicle crashes on public roads involving Volkswagens, including analyses of needed design changes indicated by the crash.

4. Summaries of all VW warranty claims to highlight weaknesses or extraordinary degradation in specific vehicle components.

5. Publication each year of the subject of owner complaint letters by vehicle component.

6. A list of all safety defect recall campaigns which were carried out for VWs anywhere in the world.

7. Complete safety performance data (crashworthiness of the vehicle, braking capability, handling etc.) in terms understandable for the motorist owner.

8. A list of all pending and decided law suits brought against Volkswagen anywhere in the world in which the issues of the suit were primarily related to safety.

### C. *Responsibilities of the National Highway Traffic Safety Administration*

The authority to set and enforce motor vehicle safety standards rests with the National Highway Traffic Safety Administration (NHTSA) in the Department of Transportation. The NHTSA is also given broad powers to investigate and require public notification of safety defects in automobiles and trucks.

The NHTSA is currently investigating the seat tracks of 1965–71 Beetles and has in the past investigated (wrongfully refusing to order defect notification) the gasoline tank cap on 1961–67 Beetles. If Volkswagen should refuse to recall its vehicles for the defects listed in Section B of this chapter, the NHTSA should immediately begin a broad-scale investigation into all of these items and into the safety of all vehicles built by VWAG and imported into this country. Such an investigation deserves a high priority because of the large numbers of Volkswagens on the American roads, and the severity of their safety defects.

The NHTSA has, in the past, written safety standards which cater to the lowest common denominator in the automotive industry. Usually the manufacturers of small foreign cars are in the forefront of the resistance to incorporation of safety features, attempting to cut costs in the economy car competition.

The most flagrant example of a lapse in federal safety standards is the exemption of multi-purpose passenger vehicles from many of the standards which must be met by conventional passenger cars. The VW microbus is all the more unsafe because it is not required to meet many of the important automobile standards, for example, the standard for head restraints. The NHTSA must immediately eliminate this loophole in the rules which ironically allows vehicles which are likely to carry more passengers to be less safe.

In addition, the federal motor vehicle safety standards should be reviewed to determine if they provide sufficient protection to passengers of smaller cars. In particular, crash testing should take into account the likelihood that a lighter car will collide with a far heavier one. Barrier collision testing should specify the initial momentum (mass times velocity) of the vehicle, rather than the initial speed, since this would properly account for the smaller mass of the compact and subcompact cars. Testing for rear-end crashworthiness should be done with standard-sized moving barriers.

Other safety standards which are in need of revision are those for seat strength (number 207), door latch strength (206), and gasoline system integrity (301). The seat strength standard should be initially upgraded by requiring higher loading of the seats, and by specifying a maximum deflection permissible before failure of either the seat back or mounting. As soon as possible after that, standard 207 should be upgraded to a performance standard comparable to the new passive restraint standard 208. Such a standard might, for example, require that when a stationary car is impacted by a 5,000-lb. barrier moving at 30 mph, the occupants would not be displaced from their seats, and that the forces on the occupants not exceed a tolerable maximum.

Until the federal motor vehicle safety standards can be made sufficiently strong to eliminate unsafe vehicles from the roads, the NHTSA should require manufacturers to provide, at the time any safety-related changes are made to their vehicles, a list of these changes, the reason for the change, and all data which the manufacturer used to evaluate the impact of the change on the safety of the vehicle.

There is a lesson in all this for the NHTSA. The agency's mission under the law is to advance vehicle safety beyond current levels in the industry. Instead the agency has allowed itself to be pressured into accepting a level consonant with the lowest common denominator of the industry. This is hardly an effective way to advance motorists' safety interests. Even more deplorably, the NHTSA, after initially progressive forays in requiring safety belts, collapsible steering assemblies, improved laminated windshields, and head restraints during 1968 and 1969 model years, has gone virtually into limbo.

Even against such weak standards, however, VW has performed miserably. Out of a very limited government compliance test program, VW still managed to fail fourteen out of twenty-five compliance tests in the last three years. If the motor vehicle safety standards are to have any meaning at all beyond their use as protective fig leaves for corporate engineering debacles, it must flow from the vigorous testing and enforcement of these standards. Up to now the government has spent more money on one moon buggy than on five years of vehicle testing for safety standard enforcement.

In the event that neither Volkswagen of America nor the NHTSA recognize their responsibilities in the matter of Volkswagen automobile safety, the four or five million owners of Volkswagens constitute a large and powerful interest group to force the issue. In the meantime, the Volkswagen Beetle and bus remain totally unacceptable as vehicles for the transport of people on our roads.

# Notes

FOREWORD

1. "U.S. New-Car Market Analysis," *Automotive News,* July 19, 1971, p. 3; and "Import Registrations," *Automotive News,* July 26, 1971, p. 3. (The data show that Oldsmobile moved well ahead of Volkswagen in 1971, having trailed slightly during 1970.)
2. "Imported Cars in Operation by Model Year," *Automotive News 1971 Almanac* (Detroit: Slocum Publishing Company, 1971), p. 70.
3. This brief history of VW is based on several books and articles, listed below:

   K. B. Hopfinger, *The Volkswagen Story* (Cambridge: Bentley, Inc., 1971).

   W. H. Nelson, *Small Wonder: The Amazing Story of the Volkswagen* (Boston: Little, Brown, 1967).

   W. R. Nitske, *The Amazing Porsche and Volkswagen Story* (New York: Comet Press Books, 1958).

   D. R. Post, *Volkswagen, Nine Lives Later* (Arcadia: Horizon House, 1966).

   "Mass Output Set for Volkswagen," *New York Times,* September 25, 1955, III, p. 1.

   "Volkswagen Town Shuns Past for Future," *New York Times,* June 3, 1968, p. 69.
4. Nordhoff died on April 12, 1968. Kurt Lotz was named his successor later in 1968.
5. "Mass Output . . . ," *New York Times.* (Plans were announced in September 1955, to assemble Volkswagen in the United States. VWoA purchased a former Studebaker-Packard assembly plant in New Brunswick, New Jersey, in late 1955, but soon thereafter—based on a recalculation of the costs—sold the plant and abandoned the scheme altogether.)
6. "Inside Detroit," *Motor Trend,* December 1970, p. 18. (More recently, warranties on all domestically produced vehicles have been cut back, most to one year or 12,000 miles. Volkswagen has retained its two-year or 24,000-mile warranty, and added a diagnostic service.)
7. The Center for Auto Safety has on file over 300 letters from Volkswagen owners complaining about problems with their

VWs and reporting their frustrations trying to get them fixed. In one case, handled by Cleveland's Auto Safety Research Center, an affiliate of the Center for Auto Safety, the owner had so many problems with his 1971 Super Beetle that VWoA's midwest distributor, MIDVW, offered him a reimbursement of $2100 for his six-month-old car which had originally cost him about $2300.

8. Volkswagen of America, Inc., *Background Data for VW Dealers* on *A Study of Volkswagen Accidents in the U.S.*, December 14, 1968, p. 11. (Sent to dealers with cover letter dated Dec. 4, 1968, signed by Arthur R. Railton, Vice President of VWoA, Inc. See also, "Facts Versus Headlines," *VW Dealer and Industry News,* February 22, 1971, p. 4, which asserts unabashedly, "So VW is a safe car.")
9. a. Wilcox v. Continental Motor Sales, Deposition of Friedrich Goes, Safety Director, VWAG, No. 810,225, Superior Court of the State of California for the County of Los Angeles, p. 3 (1968). The deposition reads:

   Q. "What was your next capacity with Volkswagen?"
   A. "In about April, 1966, I was assigned to the automotive safety task and held the position of chief safety test engineer and am now safety director . . ."
   Q. "Who preceded you as chief safety testing engineer?"
   A. "We had no special safety test group up to that point."
   Q. "Up until April, 1966?"
   A. "Yes. It was all done by all people. The safety task was done by everyone. It was part of everyone's job."

   b. "Germans to Study Safety," *New York Times,* April 27, 1966, p. 31. (The *Times* reported the formation of a joint safety committee involving Volkswagen and Daimler-Benz. The article noted that both companies have had separate teams looking into the problem.)

   c. "Volkswagen Distributor Loses $1,021,275 Verdict," *Wall Street Journal,* March 12, 1968, p. 13. (In the Wilcox case, the jury awarded $1,021,275 to a Los Angeles man whose 1956 Beetle rolled over on a right-hand curve.)

   d. "Los Angeles Jury Labels Rear Suspension Design of 1968 VW 'Defective'," *Wall Street Journal,* February 29, 1968, p. 18. (As a result of the crash, Mr. Wilcox became a paraplegic.)

   e. Arthur Railton, VWoA Vice President, claims that Mr. Goes was referring specifically to an office to monitor federal motor vehicle safety standards. He claims that there was a Volkswagen safety office before 1966 (private communication with Center for Auto Safety).
10. The multiplicity of names and model numbers attached to the Beetle and other models made by Volkswagen is sometimes confusing. To help eliminate any confusion, see Appendix II, "Volkswagen Model Designations."
11. A revealing view of the character of Volkswagen of America is afforded by examining its manner of defending law suits brought against it by persons claiming injury in VW crashes resulting from VW design defects. A variety of strategies

and tactics has been used, although not always with success.

Bollard v. VW. (District Court, W. D. Mo., Civil Action No. 17845-3, 1971.) The case alleged that in 1969 a woman received serious injuries to the head and neck because of seat and windshield defects in a VW. She sued VWoA for damages. In response, VWoA refused to answer or provided contradictory answers to questions posed before the trial by her attorney. In fact, VWoA was so uncooperative that a federal judge in Missouri granted a default judgment against the company with the comment, "This case is an example of the frustration of the judicial process . . ." The judge further added that ". . . experience has shown that . . . possibly to avoid class actions, defendants in motor vehicle products liability cases based upon defects in design and workmanship have been unusually evasive and loathe to make discovery."

12. The Corvair, like the VW, is powered by an air-cooled rear engine. GM also used the dangerous swing axle rear suspension in the 1960–1964 model Corvairs. In 1965 the rear suspension design was changed to a fully independent suspension, incorporating an extra universal joint in each axle shaft. The Corvair's heater (1961–69 models) is similar to the pre-1963 VW heater but is inferior to the later VW's. The air used to heat the Corvair and early VW interiors first passes over the engine surfaces as the coolant for the air-cooled engine. Thus a defective seal or gasket could leak carbon monoxide and other exhaust fumes into the cooling air and then into the passenger compartment. In the VW's "fresh air" heater, installed in 1963 and newer VWs, the air is warmed by flowing around the outside of the exhaust pipe, which is a finned heat exchanger that passes through the center of the heater box. Therefore, the exhaust pipe must have a leak before exhaust fumes would get into the heater air. A leak in the later VW system is less likely than in the Corvair's and early VW's forced air heaters. Tests conducted by Consumers Union bears this out. (See *Consumer Reports,* September, 1971, pp. 572–74.) A recent study performed for the U.S. Department of Transportation by the Automobile Club of Southern California indicates that pre-1963 VWs may be subject to "dangerous leakage of carbon monoxide into the passenger compartment" (*Wall St. Journal,* March 3, 1972).

## CHAPTER 1

1. Jaakko K. Kihlberg, Eugene A. Narragon, and B. J. Campbell, *Automobile Crash Injury in Relation to Car Size,* ACIR, CAL no. VJ-1823-R11 (Buffalo: Cornell Aeronautical Laboratory, Inc., 1964). (This study analyzed data from 12,835 injury-producing vehicles in rural motor vehicle crashes, grouped as follows:

    Small Cars 771 Vehicles (under 2000 lbs.) incl. 317 VWs

Compact Cars 1085 Vehicles (2000–2999 lbs.) incl. 30 VWs
Standard Cars 10,979 Vehicles (3000 lbs. and over)

The conclusions of the study are as follows:

1. Circumstances which produce 100 injured occupants in standard size vehicles produce about 106 injured occupants in compacts and about 110 in small cars.
2. When circumstances set the stage for 100 severe or fatal injuries in standard size cars, 112 will occur in compacts and 118 in small cars.
3. When crashes occur which kill 100 persons in standard cars, about 130 will be killed in compacts and 152 in small cars.

2. U.S., Department of Transportation, NHSB, *Vehicle Safety Design Surveillance System: Special Interim Report,* DOT contract no. FH-11-6799, prepared by the State of New York, Dept. of Motor Vehicles (June 3, 1969).
3. John W. Garrett and Arthur Stern, *A Study of Volkswagen Accidents in the U.S.*, ACIR, CAL no. VJ-1823-R32 (Buffalo: Cornell Aeronautical Laboratory, Inc., 1968). (Available in abridged form.)
4. *Ibid.*, p. 56. (The category "Foreign Sport" included in the study, is omitted here since these small foreign sports cars are not comparable to others included in the table. Dangerous and fatal injuries are sustained in small foreign cars at an extremely high rate per accident, slightly greater than the rate for the Beetle, though the differences between the rates for these cars and for Beetle are not statistically significant. See *Special Interim Report.*)
5. *Ibid.*, pp. 16–17. (A principal rollover is defined as an accident in which both collision and overturn of the car may occur, but major car damage is associated with the rollover.)
6. *Ibid.*, pp. 16–17. (At the time of this ACIR study, most of the Renaults on the road were the Dauphine model. The Dauphine is even more notorious for its unstable handling than the VW. For Renaults in the ACIR study the figures are as follows: 55.4 percent of all Renault crashes were rollovers and of these, 70 percent were rollovers without collision. In any accident above 34 miles per hour, the probability that the Renault would roll over was greater than 50 percent. The Dauphine model has not been imported since 1965.)
7. *Ibid.*, p. 23.
8. *Ibid.*, p. 49.
9. *Ibid.*, p. 57.
10. *Ibid.*, p. 58. (VW introduced an improved door latch on the 1965 models and made further improvements for the 1967 models, but the effectiveness of these changes has not yet been definitely evaluated. See Chapter 3.)
11. *Ibid.*, pp. 51–3.
12. *Ibid.*, p. 53.
13. *Ibid.*, p. 25.

14. *Ibid.,* p. 58.
15. *Ibid.,* in Summary section, p. viii.
16. *Ibid.,* summary of abridged version, p. i. ("Car size alone is not the major factor, however. Ejection of occupants from the vehicle with its increased risks of serious injury or death is the primary factor.")
17. *Ibid.,* unabridged version, p. 58.
18. J. G. Wall, R. N. Kemp, and J. Harris, *Comparative Head-on Impact Tests of Cars with Either Front Transverse or Rear Mounted Engines,* RRL Report LR 155 (Road Research Laboratory, Ministry of Transport, Crowthorne, Great Britain, 1970), p. 4.
19. Garrett and Stern, *A Study of Volkswagen Accidents,* pp. 25 and 45.
20. *Ibid.,* p. 105.
21. Robert A. Wolf, Transportation Research Dept., Cornell Aeronautical Laboratory, Inc., *letter* to U.S. Senator Warren G. Magnuson, January 10, 1969. (Reprinted on pp. 285–87 of *Motor Vehicle Safety—1969, Hearings* before the Committee on Commerce, U.S. Senate, on S. 1245, Ser. 91-17, 91st Cong., 1st sess., 1969.)
22. Volkswagen of America, Inc., *Background Data for VW Dealers* on *A Study of Volkswagen Accidents in the U.S.,* December 14, 1968, p. 11.
23. B. J. Campbell, *Driver Injury in Automobile Accidents Involving Certain Car Models,* University of North Carolina Highway Safety Research Center (Chapel Hill: 1970).
24. *Ibid.,* p. 32. (Index numbers are listed only if they are statistically significant in accordance with Dr. Campbell's measure of significance. The selection of makes for inclusion in the table is also that of the Campbell study. Dr. Campbell's title for the class of vehicles is "Group VI: Other Cars: Foreign, American Specialty cars, and a Re-Grouping of American Compact Cars."

    (The report [p. 19] carries the following warning: "The statistical procedures used in this study consist of testing each car model against the same aggregate reference group. This does *not* provide a direct comparison of one model to the other." For example, in the chart following this note in the text, it can be said that driver injuries in the VW Beetle for 1960–67 are significantly different from the aggregate. But this fact does not afford a comparison, for instance, between the Beetle and the Valiant. Dr. Campbell adds: "The data do, however, lend themselves to this kind of analysis [comparison of cars to each other] and such could be undertaken later." According to a statistician at the Insurance Institute for Highway Safety who consults and advises with Dr. Campbell, it is not likely that the rank order shown in the chart would change if such an analysis were undertaken.)
25. U.S., Congress, Senate, Committee on the Judiciary, *Automotive Repair Industry, Hearings* before the Subcommittee on Antitrust and Monopoly, U.S. Senate, on S. Res. 334,

pt. 4, 91st Cong., 2d sess., 1970, p. 1680. (The Campbell report, *Driver Injury in Automobile Accidents Involving Certain Car Models,* is reproduced in the Hearing book beginning on p. 1646.)

26. *Ibid.,* pp. 1576–78 as well as U.S., DOT *Special Interim Report.*
27. Ron Wakefield, "Suspension & Handling," Road & Track Special Supplement, *Road & Track,* June, 1970. (The main factors affecting instability in vehicle handling are the design of the suspension system and tires, the weight distribution, and the ratio of track to the height of the center of gravity. While this latter ratio tends to be smaller in the narrower and taller small sedans, there is no necessity for this to be the case.)
28. New Jersey Highway Authority, *Compact Car Accident Study, Garden State Parkway* (June 1969). The 1969 study concludes in part: "Volkswagen experience for the calendar year 1969 shows some improvement over 1968. Like other compacts, Volkswagen had less than its share of accidents, but somewhat more injuries than it should, especially serious injuries.

    "Although the percentage of Volkswagens involved in single-vehicle accidents dropped from 1968, its involvement rate was higher than . . . [for] compacts as a whole and standard cars [46.1% single-vehicle accidents for VWs as against 27.3% for standard sized cars in 1968; 37.1% for VW and 29.8% for standard sized cars in 1969]. Slippery roads bothered nearly 30% of [accident-involved] Volkswagen drivers . . . slightly more than last year. . . . Volkswagens show a rather high rate of overturning. . . ." (1968: VW 27.6%n Std. 2%; 1969: VW 18.6%; Std. 3.53%.)
29. K. G. Jamieson and I. A. Tait, *Report of a General Survey of Traffic Injuries in Brisbane,* Special Report Series No. 13 (Canberra, Commonwealth of Australia: National Health and Medical Research Council, 1966). (In this study, two neurosurgeons made a detailed analysis of 1000 consecutive highway crash-related admissions to hospitals or deaths in the Brisbane area over a 16-month period beginning in early 1962. The sample included 188 deaths [58 in motor vehicle crashes], 2338 individual participants, including injuries to 267 drivers, 257 passengers, and 243 pedestrians. Only major injuries were considered [defined as major fractures or visceral injuries]. The project was hospital centered, starting with the patient. The sample contained 596 motor vehicles, including 386 of known brand name, and involved 372 motor crashes.)
30. Commonwealth of Massachusetts, Registry of Motor Vehicles, *Vehicle Involvement Study* (April 1968).
31. VWoA, *Background Data,* p. 11.
32. National Safety Council, *Accident Facts* (Chicago: NSC Statistic Division, 1969).
33. Kihlberg, et al., *Automobile Crash Injury,* p. 30.
34. *Ibid.,* p. 17. (This study reviews all significant literature on this point written up through 1964.)

CHAPTER 2

1. W. F. Milliken, Jr., and David W. Whitcomb, "General Introduction to a Programme of Dynamic Research," *Research in Automobile Stability and Control and in Tyre Performance* (London: Institution of Mechanical Engineers, Automobile Division, 1956).
2. "Road & Track Owner Survey—Volkswagen Beetle," *Road & Track,* January, 1969, p. 104.
3. "How You Can Drive a Small Car Safely," *Popular Science,* July, 1971, p. 90.
4. E. E. Larrabee, "Small Scale Research in Automobile Aerodynamics" (SAE paper no. 660384, 1966), pp. 6, 7.
5. One tire with most of the weight supported by a pair of wheels on an axle has less lateral traction than two tires each with half the weight. This is depicted in the diagram below:

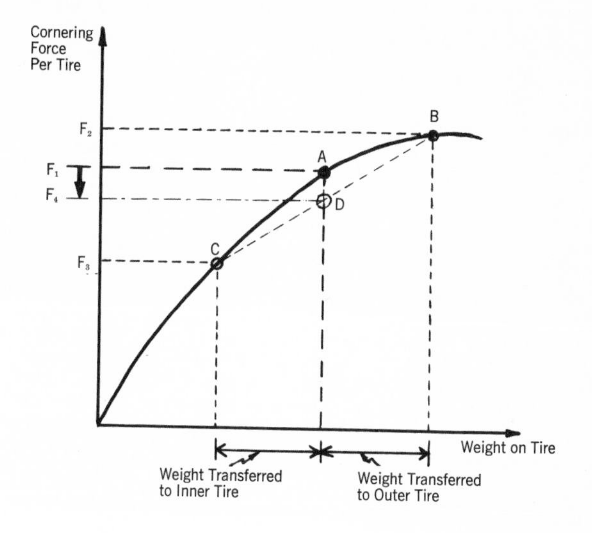


Cornering force of a tire as a function of the downward force or weight on the tire. (Cornering force is the force which makes the car turn a corner; thus the greater the cornering force, the less the tire slippage.) If both tires on an axle were equally loaded, the cornering force would be twice the force $F_1$, with each tire loaded at point A on the curve. If there is a weight transfer so that the outside tire is at point B and the inside tire is at point C, the net cornering force will be the sum of $F_2$ and $F_3$, or twice $F_4$, which is less than twice $F_1$. It can be seen from the shape of the curve that the greater the weight transfer, the lower the total cornering force.

6. Jan P. Norbye, "Vehicle Dynamics—Some Basics on Why Cars Behave the Way They Do," *Automobile Quarterly,* Fall, 1970, p. 87.
7. Garrett and Stern, *A Study of VW Accidents,* p. 23.
8. *Ibid.,* p. 17.
9. Wilcox v. Continental Motor Sales, Deposition of Friedrich Goes, Safety Director, VWAG, pp. 52–3.
10. U.S., Patent no. 2,198,978 issued April, 1940, to Chris H. Sauer.
11. U.S., Department of Transportation, NHTSA, "Tire and Rim Selection and Rim Performance, Proposed Motor Vehicle Safety Standard," *Federal Register,* XXXVI, no. 149, August 3, 1971, pp. 14273–74.
12. *VW Workshop Manual 1969, Vol. B: Brakes, Wheels, Tires, Hand and Foot Controls,* 1st supplement (Wolfsburg, Germany: Volkswagenwerk AG, 1969), p. Bl. 6:1-1. (Note that the Type II wheels are not of the safety-rim type.)
13. *Volkswagen Service Manual, VW 1300/1500* (Cambridge: Robert Bentley, Inc., 1971), p. 266.
14. *Ibid.,* p. 276.
15. *Volkswagen 1200, Instruction Manual, Sedan and Convertible* (Wolfsburg, Germany: Volkswagenwerk AG, 1964), p. 26. (The only warning in this manual with respect to the use of different types of tires and wheels is that snow tires should not be mounted on the front wheels only.)
16. Adapters are available, however, which make it possible to install almost any American wheel to any post-1951 Volkswagen. (See, for instance, *Auto Accessories & Parts Book: Catalog no. 296* [Chicago: J. C. Whitney & Co., 1971], p. 155.) While fitting an American safety rim wheel to a pre-1968 VW may solve the air-out problem, it may create others, such as increased loads on wheel bearings, wider turning circle, and altered steering geometry. Because of such side effects, it is always preferable to use wheels which do not require the use of adapters.
17. "The Little Cars," *Consumer Reports,* January, 1971, p. 8.
18. "Five Small Wagons," *Consumer Reports,* August, 1969, p. 466.
19. "Bus-Wagons," *Consumer Reports,* August, 1971, p. 500.
20. U.S., Department of Transportation, NHSB, *Effects of Steering and Suspension Degradation on Automobile Stability and Control,* ACIR (Buffalo: Cornell Aeronautical Laboratory, 1970), Part II, Vol. 5, pp. 7–9.
21. Arthur D. Little, Inc., *Review of Small-Car Safety Studies by The New Jersey Highway Authority—Garden State Parkway,* Report no. C-72248, 1971, p. 3.

CHAPTER 3

1. *Injury Exposures in a Large–Small Car Collision,* a UCLA Student Project of Engineering 104 C-D, Section 1-T, Instructors: D. M. Severy and J. D. Baird, March 14, 1969.
2. *VW Dealer & Industry News,* p. 2.

3. There is some evidence of VW seat defects relating to *front* impacts, though it is not as comprehensive as that relating to rear-end collisions.

   A Maryland attorney is representing a woman whose 1967 Beetle collided almost head-on with a 1969 Mustang. Neither car was traveling more than 10 mph. The woman gripped the steering wheel, but defective seat adjusters allowed the seat to slide forward, bruising her severely and causing the death of her baby, a 7-month-old fetus, shortly afterward. (See Schweiker v. Volkswagen of America, Pretrial Statement filed in Circuit Court for Prince George's County, Maryland.)

   An accident case reported to the NHTSA, DOT HS 600 087, described a Volkswagen seat breaking completely free of its track, "apparently sliding forward past the 'stop' device" as the 1968 VW sedan had a low-speed head-on impact with another vehicle. The case investigators added, "This type of seat failure has also been observed in 2 accidents not selected for MCR work-up. Both were low-speed head-on collisions involving Volkswagens, one a bus and the other another sedan." (See U.S., Department of Transportation, NHTSA, *Multidisciplinary Accident Investigation Summaries,* Vol. 1, no. 2, HS600087.)

   A Hawaii law firm is handling a case where the seat suddenly slid forward, pinning the client against the steering wheel and causing loss of vehicle control. (Austin v. Volkswagenwerk AG, 1st Circuit Court, State of Hawaii, Civil no. 32525, filed November 23, 1970.)

   And attorneys from New York and New Mexico are representing clients whose seats came loose in front-end collisions due to the inadequacy of the "stop" device or the weakness of the tracks. (Letters to Center for Auto Safety, dated February 25, 1971 and February 18, 1971.)

4. If we assume that the cars remain attached after the crash, and that the weights of the VW and the American car are 1800 lbs. and 4000 lbs., respectively, the momentum conservation equation gives the final speed of the VW as:

$$M_1 \times V_1 + M_2 \times V_2 = (M_1 + M_2)V_f$$
$$4000/32 \text{ slugs } (44 \text{ ft./sec.}) = 5800/32 \text{ slugs } V_f$$
$$V_f = 30.4 \text{ ft./sec.}$$

   If we now assume that the acceleration is constant and takes place in one foot of the total crush, we have:

$$V^2{}_f = 2(a)(s)$$
$$a = \frac{(30.4)^2}{2 \times 1} = 462 \text{ ft./sec.}^2$$

   Consequently, the force on the seat back due to the 150-lb. occupant is:

$$F = \frac{150}{32} \times 462 = 2165 \text{ lbs.}$$

   Assuming the seat back has a one-to-one mechanical advantage on the seat track, an upward force of at least 1000 lbs. would be exerted on each track.

5. a. Waddoups v. Volkswagenwerk AG, Circuit Court, 1st Circuit, Hawaii, Civil no. 26347 (filed October 16, 1968). (Inadequate seat design in the Squareback was recently demonstrated in the case of Waddoups v. Volkswagen AG. A stationary 1965 Squareback was rear-ended at 35–50 mph by a 1956 Chevrolet; the driver's seat came loose from its tracks, propelling the plaintiff into the rear of the vehicle and causing head injuries. The jury awarded the plaintiffs $63,000, finding Volkswagen liable for defective design of the vehicle, and apportioned the damages as follows: Volkswagen, 40 percent; operator of the Chevrolet, 60 percent.)
   b. O'Brien, T., *letter* to Center for Auto Safety, dated February 21, 1971. (A Philadelphia VW owner was stopped at a light when his 1968 Squareback was hit from behind at 25 mph or less by a tractor-trailer. The seat broke loose from the floor, and the driver suffered head and neck injuries. Although the Squareback seat track design is not the same as that of the sedan, these failures suggest it is also defective.)
6. U.S., Department of Transportation, NHSB, *Multidisciplinary Accident Investigation Summaries,* Vol. 1, no. 6, HS600-344, p. 49.
7. Waddoups v. Volkswagenwerk AG. (VWoA did not import the Squareback model into the U.S. until October, 1965. The Waddoups bought their Squareback from VW in Germany and had it shipped to Hawaii in early 1965.
8. *VW Dealer & Industry News,* Vol. 3, no. 2, February 22, 1971.
9. Garrett and Stern, *A Study of VW Accidents,* p. 53.
10. U.S., Department of Transportation, NHSB, *Comparative Crash Survivability Program Phase I Report,* DOT contract no. FH-11-6866, May, 1969, pp. 2–19, 2–20.
11. N. E. Shoemaker, D. J. Segal, and K. N. Naab, *An Experimental Evaluation of the 1969 Volkswagen 1500 Restraint System and Front Seat Assembly,* ACIR, CAL no. YB-2684-V-100 (Buffalo: Cornell Aeronautical Laboratory, Inc., 1969).
12. *Ibid.,* p. 2.
13. Jack Anderson, "Volkswagen Design Results in Deadly Ejector-Seat Effect," *Chicago Daily News,* February 9, 1971.
14. Derwyn M. Severy, Harrison M. Brink, and Jack D. Baird, "Backrest and Head Restraint Design for Rear-End Collision Protection." (SAE Preprint 680079, 1968), p. 91.
15. *Injury Exposures in a Large–Small Car Collision,* p. 48.
16. *Ibid.,* pp. 3–4.
17. a. Derwyn M. Severy, Harrison Brink and Jack Baird, "Collision Performance, LM Safety Car" (SAE Preprint 670458, 1967).
   b. Roger P. Daniel, "Vehicle Interior Safety Constraint Systems" (SAE Preprint 700423: *International Automobile Safety Conference Compendium,* 1970), p. 1052.
18. U.S. Department of Commerce, National Traffic Safety

Agency, "Report on the Development of the Initial Federal Motor Vehicle Safety Standards Issued January 31, 1967," Washington, D.C., March 1967, p. 82. The General Services Administration (GSA) sets standards for vehicles purchased by the federal government. The Society of Automotive Engineers (SAE) sets recommended practices or standards for the auto industry. These are usually followed voluntarily by domestic auto manufacturers, which is not surprising as SAE is little more than an arm of the American automobile industry.

19. a. Severy, "Collision Performance."
    b. Severy, "Backrest."
    c. Derwyn M. Severy, et al., "Safer Seat Design," *Proceedings,* 13th Stapp Car Crash Conference, December 2–4, 1969, Boston, Massachusetts.
20. Severy, "Collision Performance."
21. *Ibid.,* p. 609.
22. U.S., Congress, Senate, Commerce Committee, *Motor Vehicle Safety Standards, Hearings* before the Committee on Commerce, U.S. Senate, Serial no. 90-36, 90th Cong., 1st sess., 1967, pp. 168–69 and p. 181.
23. Severy, "Backrest."
24. Severy, "Safer Seat Design."
25. J. O. Moore and B. Tourin, *A Study of Automobile Doors Opening Under Crash Conditions* (New York: Cornell University Medical College ACIR Study, 1954), p. ii.
26. B. Tourin, "Ejection and Automobile Fatalities," *Public Health Reports,* Vol. 73, no. 5 (May, 1958), p. 383.
27. Huelke and Gikas, "Ejection—The Leading Cause of Death in Automobile Accidents" (SAE paper no. 660802, 1966).
28. U.S., Department of Transportation, NHSB, *Monthly Progress Report of Research Activity in Occupant Restraint Systems, March, 1969.*
29. U.S., Department of Transportation, NHSB, *Performance Requirements for Doors, Door Retaining Devices and Adjacent Structures,* by Bartol, Wingenbach, Hodosy, et al., DOT contract no. FH-11-6891 (1969), p. 11–4.
30. U.S., Department of Transportation, NHSB, *Test Procedures and Requirements for Door System Evaluation,* by Dale and Seal, DOT contract no. HS-005-1-005 (1971), p. 10.
31. Gross, "Accidental Motorist Ejection and Door Latching Systems" (SAE paper no. 640165, 1964), p. 5–6.
32. Garrett and Stern, *A Study of VW Accidents,* p. 66.
33. U.S., Department of Transportation, NHSB, *Comparison of Door Opening Frequency in 1967–1968 Cars with Earlier Model U.S. Cars,* by J. W. Garrett, DOT contract no. FH-11-7098 (1969).

    J. W. Garrett, *An Evaluation of Door Lock Effectiveness: Pre-1956 vs. Post-1955 Automobiles,* ACIR (Buffalo: Cornell Aeronautical Laboratory).

    J. W. Garrett, *The Safety Performance of 1962–63 Automobile Door Latches and Comparison with Earlier Latch*

*Design,* ACIR CAL no. VJ-1823-R7 (Buffalo: Cornell Aeronautical Laboratory, 1964).
34. U.S., DOT, *Comparison of Door Opening Frequency,* p. 5.
35. Garrett and Stern, *A Study of VW Accidents,* p. 46.
36. *Ibid.,* p. 16.
37. *Ibid.,* p. 66.
38. *Ibid.,* p. 50.
39. *Ibid.,* p. 49.
40. *Ibid.,* p. 48.
41. U.S., DOT, *Performance Requirements for Doors,* p. 8–1.
42. *Ibid.,* p. 8–13.
43. John W. Norvel, Chief, Equipment Supplier Branch, Verification Division, Office of Standards Enforcement, NHTSA, phone interview, August 31, 1971.
44. U.S., Congress, Senate, Committee on Government Operations, *Federal Role in Traffic Safety, Part 2, Hearings* before the Subcommittee on Executive Reorganization of the Committee on Government Operations, U.S. Senate, 89th Cong., 1st sess., 1965, p. 789.
45. U.S., DOT, *Comparison of Door Opening Frequency,* p. 6.
46. *VW Dealer and Industry News,* February 22, 1971, p. 2.
47. German Patent 1,010,858, p. 1.
48. French Patent 1,149,646 issued December, 1957, to Ford Motor Company; British Patent 735,055 issued August, 1955, to Wilmot-Breeden, Ltd.; German Patent 1,065,749 issued September, 1959, to J. H. Roethel; U.S. Patent 2,944,850, filed for in February, 1956 by J. H. Roethel, issued July, 1960. Copies available from U.S. Patent Office, Arlington, Virginia.
49. *Automotive News 1971 Almanac* (Detroit: Slocum Publishing Company, 1971), p. 70.

CHAPTER 4

1. Garrett and Stern, *A Study of VW Accidents,* p. 18. In the Cornell study 62.3 percent of the Beetles were most severely damaged in the frontal area.
2. R. Brenner, Acting Director, NHSTA, *letter* to G. Storbeck, Product Planning Manager, VWoA, on fuel line severing, December 18, 1969.
3. D. Toms, Director, NHSTA, *letter* to G. Storbeck, VWoA, on jack-caused rupture, May 4, 1970.
4. William I. Stieglitz Associates, "Evaluation of Fuel Tank Design and Installation, Volkswagen Beetle" (unpublished report, 1968), pp. 1–2.
5. *Ibid.,* p. 3.
6. Tanner v. Volkswagenwerk AG, Deposition of Ulreich Seiffert, Civil no. 7925, U.S. District Court, New Mexico (February 10, 1971). (This case stems from a crash in Albuquerque, New Mexico, in September 1967, in which two occupants of a 1966 VW were killed when it allegedly rolled, lost its cap, and then caught fire.)

7. Swedish Council on Road Safety, "Test No. 2, at Impact Velocity of 52.9 kilometers per hour" (Stockholm, Sweden: SCRS, Traffic Medicine, FACK). (Summary of report available in Public File, "VW Gas Cap Investigation," Technical Reference Section, Room 5108, U.S., DOT NHTSA.)
8. Bengt Pontén, "Burns in Automobile Accidents," *Scandinavian Journal of Plastic Reconstructive Surgery,* Vol. 2, 1968, p. 108. (Reproduced in Appendix VIII.)
9. *Ibid.*
10. U.S., Department of Transportation, NHSB, *Comparative Crash Survivability Program, Phase I Report,* DOT contract no. FH-11-6866, prepared by Measurement Analysis Corporation, a subsidiary of Digitek Corporation (May, 1969), pp. 2–18, 2–19, 3–32, and 3–33.
11. U.S., Department of Transportation, NHSB, *Impact Intrusion Characteristics of Fuel Systems,* DOT contract no. FH-11-7309, prepared by A. F. Brayman, Jr., ACIR, CAL no. VJ-2839-K (Buffalo: Cornell Aeronautic Laboratory, Inc., 1970), p. 12.
12. *Ibid.,* p. 20.
13. U.S., Department of Transportation, NHSB, *Fuel Tank Protection, An Investigation of Fuel Exhaust, and Electrical Systems as Related to Post Crash Fire Safety,* DOT contract no. FH-11-6919, prepared by Fairchild-Hiller Division, Republic Aviation (June, 1969).
14. Tanner v. VWAG.
15. New York State Department of Motor Vehicles, *Volkswagen Fatal Fire Accidents 1967* (August, 1968), p. 5.
16. *Ibid.*
17. The full report is available at the National Highway Traffic Safety Administration, Washington, D.C., 20591. These figures are based on data found on p. 4 of the September, 1968, version. The figure 1.11 percent for "all other vehicles" is arrived at by subtracting from figures in the category "total vehicle summary," the figures for Volkswagen (128 vehicle crashes, 3 fires), and recomputing the percentage with the VW data eliminated.
18. Garrett and Stern, *A Study of VW Accidents,* p. 35.
19. University of Oklahoma Research Institute, "Multidisciplinary Investigations to Evaluate the Escape Worthiness of Vehicles for Occupancy Survivals and Crashes," Monthly Report no. 1770-MR-2, pursuant to DOT contract no. FH-11-7512 (August, 1970), pp. 1–2. (This criticism of the Cornell ACIR data cites serious inconsistencies in the data.) See also, U.S., Department of Transportation, NHTSA, *Escape Worthiness of Vehicles and Occupant Survival, Final Report,* DOT contract no. FH-11-7303, prepared by the University of Oklahoma Research Institute (December, 1970), pp. 2–54 and 2–55.
20. "A Partial Listing of Motor Vehicle Accidents Involving Fire." Available from NHTSA, Technical Reference Rm. 5108.
21. U.S., DOT, *Impact Intrusion Characteristics,* p. 4.

CHAPTER 5

1. B. J. Campbell, *Driver Injury in Automobile Accidents.* See also, *New York Times,* n. 4 below.
2. "Bus Wagons," *Consumer Reports,* August, 1971, p. 494. ("Most subcompact sedans, including the VW Beetle, can accelerate from rest to 60 mph in 20 seconds or less. . . . But the VW bus required an excruciating 33 seconds to reach 60 mph." A comparable Ford van tested reached 60 mph in 16 seconds, the Chevrolet in 13.5.)
3. *Ibid.*
4. "Study Links Car Size and Risk of Injury," *New York Times,* March 18, 1970, p. 93.
5. "Bus Wagons," *Consumer Reports,* p. 494.
6. *Ibid.*
7. *Ibid.*, p. 493.
8. *Ibid.*, p. 501.
9. See *Federal Motor Vehicle Safety Standards:* 114 (Theft Protection), 202 (Head Restraints), and 208 (Seat Belt Assemblies).
10. U.S., Department of Transportation, NHTSA, *Code of Federal Regulations, Federal Motor Vehicle Safety Standards,* Section §571.3, Definitions. (A forward control vehicle is defined as "a configuration in which more than half of the engine length is rearward of the foremost point of the windshield base and the steering wheel hub is in the forward quarter of the vehicle length." Forward control vehicles fall under the more general category of "Multipurpose passenger vehicles.")
11. "Motor Vehicle Safety Standard No. 208," sections S4.2.2 and S4.2.3, Docket 69-7, Notice 9, *Federal Register,* Vol. 36, March 10, 1971, p. 4604. (These sections carve out an exception for such forward control vehicles, and allow them to use seat belt assemblies alone without testing for the added occupant protection required of most other types of vehicles. This standard is currently being appealed by the automobile industry, but on other grounds.)
12. a. *New York Times,* August 24, 1966, p. 23. (Enders v. VWAG, et al., Madison, Wisconsin, Circuit Court, filed August 1966. In this case the plaintiff alleged that the front end and bumper failed to prevent penetration of the passenger compartment and that the front panel of the vehicle struck and injured her legs.)
    b. Bewley v. VWoA et al., Superior Court of New Jersey, Camden County, Docket no. L-9163-69, filed November 1969. (In this case the driver of a VW bus traveling at low speed sustained serious leg injuries when the bus ran into a bridge abutment.)
13. Volkswagenwerk AG, "Home on the Range," VW Campmobile Advertising Pamphlet No. 33-23-86020 (printed in U.S.A.). (It is interesting to note that the most recent edition of this pamphlet, No. 33-23-16010, which is virtually

unchanged from the earlier edition, does *not* claim that the campmobile has a safety latch for the rear door. After learning of the hazard, VW chose to eliminate the false claim rather than install a two-stage latch assembly.)

CHAPTER 6

1. Indexes of compliance testing are available to the public at the Department of Transportation, National Highway Traffic Safety Administration, Technical Reference, Room 5108, Washington, D.C.
2. Letter, Robert Brenner, Acting Director National Highway Safety Bureau, to G. Storbeck, Product Planning Manager Volkswagen of America, dated December 18, 1969 (reproduced in Appendix V).
3. Intext, Transportation Research Division, *Automobile Defect Recall Campaigns, A Survey of Time Phased Effectiveness and Owner Satisfaction* (Scranton, Pa., May 1970), prepared for the U.S. Department of Transportation National Highway Safety Bureau, under contract FH-11-6939.
4. *Ibid.,* Table 3, p. T-1.
5. *Ibid.,* Table 10, p. T-8.
6. *Ibid.,* Table 14, p. T-12.
7. The designation "IR 60" stands for Information Request number 60. An information request is sent to an auto company by the Office of Defects Investigation, National Highway Traffic Safety Administration, when it seeks test data, warranty claims data or other information as a part of a defect investigation. The file for each investigation, including "IRs," is made public when the investigation is closed, and is available for viewing at the NHTSA, 400 Seventh St. S.W., Washington, D.C. 20591.
8. "Volkswagen Warranty Circular #25/70, June 12, 1970," VWoA, Inc., Englewood Cliffs, N.J.

CHAPTER 7

1. *Automotive News 1971 Almanac* (Detroit: Slocum Publishing Company, 1971), p. 70. (The phrase "in significant use" excludes those vehicle makes constituting less than one half of one percent of the passenger vehicle population in the U.S. or less than 500,000 in round figures. The Renault Dauphine, the only vehicle which consistently ranked in comparable statistics in rollover, ejection, and frequency of fires in accidents as more hazardous than the Beetle, has a U.S. population of about 100,000. A chart showing numbers of imports in operation by brand name is included in Appendix I.

   Also eliminated from the conclusion are pre-1956 U.S. vehicles, included in the Cornell study, on the presumption that this population is of relatively minor significance in 1971. Some categories of pre-1956 U.S. models ranked worse than the VW by two measures, door opening and dislodged seats.

It should also be noted that Volkswagen and Renault are the only specific brand names separately identified in the data. All other individual makes are included in various groupings of vehicles, and comparative data are provided only for such groups as a whole, e.g., light U.S. sedans, standard U.S. sedans, etc.

2. The net expense to VW is, of course, much less after deductions and tax write-offs.

# *Appendix*

# APPENDIX I: IMPORTED CARS IN OPERATION BY MODEL YEAR

Imported Cars in Operation by Model Year
*(as of Jan. 1, 1971)*

| | *1970* | *1969* | *1968* | *1967* | *1966* | *1965 and earlier* | *Total* |
|---|---|---|---|---|---|---|---|
| Alfa Romeo | 1,417 | 1,826 | 1,036 | 1,710 | 1,376 | 7,724 | 15,089 |
| Audi | 6,173 | | | | | | 6,173 |
| Austin | 13,843 | 15,142 | 9,031 | 1,502 | 1,205 | 12,254 | 52,977 |
| Austin-Healey | 1,196 | 5,773 | 4,985 | 7,644 | 7,406 | 44,360 | 71,364 |
| BMW | 10,747 | 9,457 | 7,498 | 3,554 | 854 | 3,299 | 35,409 |
| Borgward | | | | | | 5,175 | 5,175 |
| Capri | 15,613 | | | | | | 15,613 |
| Citroën | 1,209 | 1,040 | 906 | 849 | 983 | 6,527 | 11,514 |
| Datsun | 100,038 | 57,458 | 38,799 | 31,453 | 18,754 | 19,097 | 265,599 |
| DKW | | | | | | 4,661 | 4,661 |
| English Ford | 9,979 | 20,321 | 22,011 | 15,420 | 6,935 | 50,866 | 125,532 |
| Fiat | 37,615 | 41,117 | 29,117 | 15,155 | 7,619 | 61,005 | 191,628 |
| Honda | 3,419 | | | | | | 3,419 |
| Jaguar | 7,246 | 5,436 | 5,025 | 5,660 | 4,120 | 25,611 | 53,098 |
| Lotus | 750 | 497 | 330 | 299 | 279 | 325 | 2,480 |
| Mazda | 2,305 | | | | | | 2,305 |
| Mercedes-Benz | 32,697 | 25,670 | 26,192 | 21,212 | 17,457 | 74,489 | 197,717 |
| Metropolitan | | | | | | 18,751 | 18,751 |
| MG | 31,359 | 21,356 | 17,145 | 20,898 | 19,007 | 88,537 | 198,302 |

Appendix I: *Continued*

Imported Cars in Operation by Model Year
(*as of Jan. 1, 1971*)

| | *1970* | *1969* | *1968* | *1967* | *1966* | *1965 and earlier* | *Total* |
|---|---|---|---|---|---|---|---|
| Morris | | | 168 | 810 | 87 | 18,444 | 19,509 |
| NSU | 363 | 217 | 300 | 514 | 478 | 2,236 | 4,108 |
| Opel | 82,856 | 90,466 | 79,835 | 50,331 | 29,064 | 62,245 | 394,797 |
| Peugeot | 5,279 | 4,227 | 4,246 | 3,765 | 2,890 | 26,392 | 46,799 |
| Porsche | 13,489 | 7,255 | 7,506 | 6,397 | 6,010 | 21,063 | 61,720 |
| Renault | 19,650 | 17,259 | 17,928 | 18,607 | 9,958 | 131,114 | 214,516 |
| Rolls Royce | 340 | 414 | 359 | 338 | 178 | 2,777 | 4,406 |
| Rootes | 1,738 | 2,524 | 2,293 | 7,267 | 7,303 | 52,594 | 73,719 |
| Rover | 1,474 | 1,352 | 2,187 | 2,584 | 1,919 | 3,048 | 12,564 |
| Saab | 11,422 | 10,432 | 10,516 | 10,021 | 6,182 | 21,196 | 69,769 |
| Simca | 5,733 | 7,042 | 4,532 | 6,778 | 10,691 | 45,831 | 80,607 |
| Subaru | 4,780 | 2,326 | | | | | 7,106 |
| Toyota | 184,158 | 115,853 | 66,364 | 30,830 | 13,581 | 3,846 | 414,632 |
| Triumph | 16,451 | 16,518 | 17,833 | 14,448 | 14,904 | 81,739 | 161,893 |
| Vauxhall | | | | | | 16,731 | 16,731 |
| Volkswagen | 579,469 | 556,422 | 555,188 | 433,187 | 399,553 | 1,382,100 | 3,905,919 |
| Volvo | 48,137 | 36,386 | 38,395 | 32,352 | 23,324 | 81,880 | 260,474 |
| Miscellaneous | 103 | 429 | 1,059 | 737 | 1,039 | 19,906 | 23,273 |
| *Total* | 1,251,048 | 1,074,215 | 970,784 | 744,322 | 613,156 | 2,395,823 | 7,049,348 |

From: *Automotive News 1971 Almanac* (Slocum Publishing Co., Detroit, Michigan, now Crain Communications, Detroit, Michigan), p. 70. 

# APPENDIX II: VOLKSWAGEN MODEL DESIGNATIONS

Volkswagen produces several model lines, and within each, there are many variations on the basic theme. To minimize any confusion, the more common name and number designations are set out here.

*1. Volkswagen Sedan*

Popularly known as the Beetle or the Bug, Volkswagen's official designation for the sedan model is Type I or Series 100. There are more than a dozen types of Beetles, and these types are shown in the chart on the next page.

VW Beetles are sometimes referred to as the VW 1200, VW 1300, and VW 1500. The numbers indicate cubic centimeters of displacement, an indicator of engine size. Beetles in the model years 1961 through 1965 were equipped with 1200 cc engines. Only the 1966 models came with a 1300 cc engine. A 1500 cc engine was introduced with the 1967 models. The jump from 1200 to 1300 cc's boosted the engine from 40 to 50 horsepower; the move to the 1500 cc engine added three more, giving the 1967 engine 53 horsepower.

*2. Volkswagen Bus*

VW refers to the bus as a Type II or Series 200. When fitted out as a passenger vehicle, VW literature calls it a station wagon, or "kombi" when ordered with five seats rather than the usual seven. As a live-in vehicle, it is called the campmobile or "camper" or "caravan." Popularly, all types tend to be called "VW bus" or "van" or "microbus." Four varieties of VW trucks built with a basic bus shape are available. Type II's have been imported to the U.S. since 1950.

*3. VW Fastback and Squareback Sedans*

The Fastback and Squareback models are Type III's or Series 300, in company language. Initially the Type III was called the VW 1500, but after the introduction of the 1600 cc engine with the 1966 Type III models and the boost of the Beetle's engine size to 1500 cc in 1967, the designation no longer applied. The Type III is somewhat larger and heavier than the Beetle, but is smaller than the bus. In Europe the Type III Squareback Sedan is called the "Variant."

Type III's were introduced in Germany in 1961, and in the U.S. in October 1965.

*4. Others*

VW recently introduced its 411 (Type IV) Series into the U.S. and has other configurations in the works. The Karmann Ghia sports car, introduced in the U.S. in 1955,

Types of Beetles
VW 1200, VW 1300, and VW 1500

| *Type* | | *Engine* | | | | *Official* |
|---|---|---|---|---|---|---|
| *A* | *B* | *Std.* | *or* | *Trans-mission* | *Designation* | *Type Designation* |
| 111 | 112 | 2 | 3 | 1 | VW 1200 | |
| 115 | 116 | 2 | 3 | 1 | VW 1200 with steel sliding roof | |
| 113 | 114 | 3 | 2 | 1 | VW 1300 | 11 |
| 117 | 118 | 3 | 2 | 1 | VW 1300 with steel sliding roof | |
| 113 | 114 | 5 | 4 | 1 | VW 1500 | |
| 117 | 118 | 5 | 4 | 1 | VW 1500 with steel sliding roof | |
| 113 | 114 | 5 | 4 | 2 | VW Automatic | |
| 117 | 118 | 6 | 4 | 2 | VW Automatic with steel sliding roof | |

*Engine* 2 = 1200 cc
3 = 1300 cc
4 = 1500 cc with exhaust control
5 = 1500 cc

*Transmission* 1 = Four-speed manual
2 = Selector automatic
3 = Automatic

is basically a Type I vehicle with a different shell. A Karmann Ghia model was also made on the Type III chassis, but was not implemented. An earlier version of the Type III Fastback, a sedan without a fastback rear sloping roof, known as the VW 1500 Sedan, has never been officially imported to the U.S. by VW, but many have come to the U.S. in private hands. The Type III Sedan or 1500 Sedan was evaluated in the October 1962 issue of *Consumer Reports*. The Porsche 914 mid-ship engine sports car is available as a VW in disguise, when equipped with a VW engine.

See also Appendix IV, "How to Tell the Year of Any Beetle."

# APPENDIX III: VOLKSWAGEN PRODUCTION FIGURES 1945–1970

## VOLKSWAGEN

| Year | Total Production: Total | Cars | Trucks & Station Wagons* | Total inside Germany | Total outside Germany | Total Exported from Germany | U.S. Registrations: Cars | Trucks** | Total | Year |
|---|---|---|---|---|---|---|---|---|---|---|
| 1945 | 1,785 | 1,785 | — | 1,785 | — | — | — | — | — | 1945 |
| 1946 | 10,020 | 10,020 | — | 10,020 | — | — | — | — | — | 1946 |
| 1947 | 8,987 | 8,987 | — | 8,987 | — | 1,656 | — | — | — | 1947 |
| 1948 | 19,244 | 19,244 | — | 19,244 | — | 4,464 | — | — | — | 1948 |
| 1949 | 46,154 | 46,146 | 8 | 46,154 | — | 7,128 | 2 | — | 2 | 1949 |
| 1950 | 90,038 | 81,979 | 8,059 | 90,038 | — | 29,387 | 157 | — | 157 | 1950 |
| 1951 | 105,712 | 93,709 | 12,003 | 105,712 | — | 35,742 | 390 | — | 390 | 1951 |
| 1952 | 136,013 | 114,348 | 21,665 | 136,013 | — | 46,881 | 601 | 10 | 611 | 1952 |
| 1953 | 179,740 | 151,323 | 28,417 | 179,740 | — | 68,754 | 980 | 33 | 1,013 | 1953 |
| 1954 | 242,373 | 202,174 | 40,199 | 242,373 | — | 108,839 | 6,343 | 271 | 6,614 | 1954 |

| | | | | | | | | | | |
|---|---|---|---|---|---|---|---|---|---|---|
| 1955 | 329,893 | 279,986 | 49,907 | 329,893 | — | 177,657 | 28,907 | 2,021 | 30,928 | 1955 |
| 1956 | 395,690 | 333,190 | 62,500 | 395,690 | — | 217,683 | 50,457 | 5,233 | 55,690 | 1956 |
| 1957 | 472,554 | 380,561 | 91,993 | 472,554 | — | 270,987 | 64,803 | 14,721 | 79,524 | 1957 |
| 1958 | 553,399 | 451,526 | 101,873 | 549,710 | 3,689 | 315,717 | 79,038 | 25,268 | 104,306 | 1958 |
| 1959 | 696,860 | 575,407 | 121,453 | 688,477 | 8,383 | 404,185 | 120,442 | 30,159 | 150,601 | 1959 |
| 1960 | 865,858 | 725,939 | 139,919 | 841,043 | 24,815 | 489,272 | 159,995 | 31,377 | 191,372 | 1960 |
| 1961 | 1,007,113 | 838,513 | 168,600 | 959,773 | 47,340 | 533,420 | 177,308 | 26,555 | 203,863 | 1961 |
| 1962 | 1,184,675 | 1,004,338 | 180,337 | 1,112,424 | 72,251 | 627,613 | 192,570 | 30,170 | 222,740 | 1962 |
| 1963 | 1,209,591 | 1,020,297 | 189,294 | 1,132,080 | 77,511 | 685,763 | 240,143 | 36,865 | 277,008 | 1963 |
| 1964 | 1,410,715 | 1,210,390 | 200,325 | 1,276,135 | 134,580 | 797,468 | 307,173 | 36,090 | 343,263 | 1964 |
| 1965 | 1,542,654 | 1,352,778 | 189,876 | 1,409,933 | 132,721 | 851,114 | 383,978 | 4,614** | 388,592 | 1965 |
| 1966 | 1,583,239 | 1,391,866 | 191,373 | 1,431,114 | 152,125 | 964,576 | 420,018 | 3,627** | 423,645 | 1966 |
| 1967 | 1,290,328 | 1,127,587 | 162,741 | 1,115,426 | 174,902 | 812,959 | 452,937 | 3,294** | 456,231 | 1967 |
| 1968 | 1,707,402 | 1,453,483 | 253,919 | 1,489,281 | 218,121 | 1,104,752 | 563,522 | 4,453** | 567,975 | 1968 |
| 1969 | 1,830,018 | 1,556,884 | 273,134 | 1,579,654 | 250,364 | 1,098,893 | 537,933 | 2,690** | 540,623 | 1969 |
| 1970 | 1,898,422 | 1,610,411 | 288,011 | 1,573,677 | 324,745 | 1,060,042 | 569,182 | 2,259** | 571,441 | 1970 |
| 1971 | 2,071,533 | 1,794,030 | 277,503 | 1,585,425 | 486,108 | 1,154,652 | 509,207 | 2,188** | 511,395 | 1971 |
| Totals | 20,890,010 | 17,836,901 | 3,053,104 | 18,782,355 | 2,107,655 | 11,869,604 | 4,866,086 | 261,898 | 5,127,984 | Totals |

* Box-shaped station wagons known in Europe as Micobuses.

** Volkswagen bus-like station wagons which were included in truck registrations through 1964 have been included in passenger car statistics since then and accounted for 62,508 of the 509,207 VW passenger cars registered during 1971.

Volkswagen Type II (Microbuses and Trucks)
Approximate U.S. Sales Figures

| *Model Year* | *No. of Vehicles* | *Model Year* | *No. of Vehicles* |
|---|---|---|---|
| 1950 | 2 | 1961 | 26,697 |
| 1951 | 50 | 1962 | 31,197 |
| 1952 | 93 | 1963 | 38,238 |
| 1953 | 75 | 1964 | 37,239 |
| 1954 | 827 | 1965 | 37,796 |
| 1955 | 3,189 | 1966 | 35,439 |
| 1956 | 6,666 | 1967 | 34,247 |
| 1957 | 18,366 | 1968 | 50,756 |
| 1958 | 24,478 | 1969 | 52,823 |
| 1959 | 32,423 | 1970 | 65,069 |
| 1960 | 34,878 | 1971 | 64,696 |

Total number of Type II Vehicles sold in the U.S.: 595,244.

Volkswagen Type III (Squareback and Fastback)
Approximate U.S. Sales Figures

| *Calendar Year* | *No. of Vehicles* |
|---|---|
| 1966 (last 2½ months) | 9,434 |
| 1967 | 69,202 |
| 1968 | 95,528 |
| 1969 (first 9½ months) | 77,352 |

## APPENDIX IV:
## HOW TO TELL THE YEAR OF ANY BEETLE

Prior to 1955, all Volkswagens were built according to calendar year. On August 1, 1955 "model years" were designated. All cars produced before the 1965 model year were numbered consecutively (see table below).

On 1965–1969 model Beetles a nine- or ten-digit (a tenth digit was added when production exceeded one million) chassis number is used for identification. The first two digits represent the model, being the same as the first two digits of the model number. The third digit is the last numeral of the model year. The remaining digits are the production numbers, indicating approximate time of manufacture during that model year.

Effective with the 1970 model year, all VWs have ten-digit identification numbers to comply with federal regulations. The first two digits of this serial number signify the model, and the third digit is the last numeral of the model year, as before. The last seven digits indicate the consecutive production number within each type.

The only positive identification of the year of a Beetle is the chassis number. This can be found in one or more locations:

1) Under the rear seat, stamped on the frame tunnel.

2) For the Beetle, on the chassis identification plate which is behind the spare tire.

3) For the Super Beetle, on the chassis identification plate which is under the front hood next to the hood lock.

4) On all vehicles produced since January 1, 1969, on the vehicle identification plate which is fastened to the dashboard near the lower left hand corner of the windshield.

The following table provides a correlation between chassis number and year:

| *Year* | *Chassis Numbers* | *Year* | *Chassis Numbers* |
|---|---|---|---|
| 1949 | 91 922 to 138 554 | 1961 | 3 192 507 to 4 010 994 |
| 1950 | 138 555 to 220 471 | 1962 | 4 010 995 to 4 846 835 |
| 1951 | 220 472 to 313 829 | 1963 | 4 846 836 to 5 677 118 |
| 1952 | 313 830 to 428 156 | 1964 | 5 677 119 to 6 502 399 |
| 1953 | 428 157 to 575 414 | 1965 | 115 000 001 to 115 979 200 |
| 1954 | 575 415 to 722 934 | 1966 | 116 000 001 to 116 1 021 198 |
| 1955 | 722 935 to 929 745 | 1967 | 117 000 001 to 117 844 892 |
| 1956 | 929 746 to 1 246 618 | 1968 | 118 000 001 to 118 1 016 098 |
| 1957 | 1 246 619 to 1 600 439 | 1969 | 119 000 001 to 119 1 093 704 |
| 1958 | 1 600 440 to 2 007 615 | 1970 | 110 2000001 to 110 3096945 |
| 1959 | 2 007 616 to 2 528 667 | 1971 | 111 2000001 to 111 3143118 |
| 1960 | 2 528 668 to 3 192 506 | 1972 | 112 2000001— |

**Source: VWoA pamphlet 13-00-01251, "What Year Is It?"**

Positive identification of the year of a *new* VW may be important. Each year approximately 3,000–6,000 Beetles are reconditioned in various parts of Europe by private firms and bootlegged into the United States and sold by unauthorized dealers as new cars. This constitutes a safety hazard because few of these vehicles meet the federal motor vehicle safety standards. Volkswagen is reluctant to prosecute these firms, fearing such action might muddy the Beetle's cultivated image of year-to-year similarity, in sharp contrast to Detroit's annual style change. Thus Volkswagen perpetuates the myth that the Beetle can approach engineering perfection while remaining virtually unchanged. Materials relating to this serious problem will be found on the following pages.

February 7, 1969

Hon. Warren Magnuson
Chairman, Senate Commerce Committee
United States Senate
Washington, D.C.

Dear Senator Magnuson:

Your Committee's jurisdiction over the Federal Trade Commission and the Committee's recently declared intention to investigate aspects of the foreign small car import problem make it appropriate for the following information to be brought to your attention for further inquiry:

For nearly a decade, unauthorized Volkswagen dealers have been selling tens of thousands of *used* Volkswagens as *new* Volkswagens to the economic disadvantage and hazard of defrauded car buyers in this country. The Volkswagen company has been fully aware of the details and dimensions of this practice since the early Sixties, has discussed the matter when called by the FTC, but has avoided public disclosure and legal action. The company has adhered to this policy so as not to incur adverse reflection on Volkswagen new car sales.

The Federal Trade Commission began an investigation of this multi-million dollar Volkswagen black-market in 1963, continued it intensively in 1964 only to have staff recommendations for prosecution and other legal action overruled by William W. Rogal, now Assistant Director of the Division of General Practices and his immediate superior, Michael J. Vitale, now Chief of the Division of General Practices. Continuing complaints and evidence coming to the Commission since the abrupt cessation of the 1963–64 investigation led to renewed inquiries by the staff. It is now clear that the practice of selling used VWs as new VWs is still prevalent and still escaping action by the Federal Trade Commission.

FTC staff investigators have documented with much detail an efficient network of trading in used VWs as new VWs, beginning in West Germany and ending in outrageous fleecing of unsuspecting car buyers who thought they were purchasing new VWs when in fact these VWs had been used previously by motorist-consumers in West Germany. Some of these used cars being sold as new over recent years had been in serious crashes in West Germany or other neighboring countries; many more had been driven thousands of miles by their first owner.

These used VWs were then taken to highly sophisticated reconditioning garages in the Hamburg area where they were prepared for shipment to the United States. Large importing firms (large in volume handled but small in overhead), particularly in New York City, would then sell them as used cars to unauthorized VW dealers throughout the United States. These dealers would then make a handsome profit by reselling them as new to customers. FTC investigators, who concentrated their attention in the greater Washington, D.C. area (including the Virginia and Maryland suburbs), reported to their superiors the methods used to deceive consumers through advertising and oral representations by salesmen and concluded that such deception was engaged in knowingly and systematically by the managers and owners of the dealerships. Used VWs were sold under advertisements using such phrases as "Fresh Shipment," "New Importations" and the like. Other techniques of deception involved near zero speedometer readings on these used VWs, price labels resembling new car labels, or false explanations about, for example, customer-observed rust being due to salt water contact during overseas shipment. In most cases, the reconditioning achieved a high degree of superficial acceptability.

Some of the cases involved these used VWs breaking down on the highways, and accidents where serious injuries were incurred, according to the FTC investigation. The Commission staff made inquiries in other states and concluded that the fraud was nationwide with various fluctuations in these deceptive sales.

Various factors combined to make the sale of used Volkswagens as new a lucrative business. The "Beetle" changed very little from year to year. Even the most recent most observable change—the high seats—offers little impediment to being used in the same manner. Second, waiting periods between ordering and delivering a VW have been longer than for domestic cars—in some periods as long as 6 months. Even periods of delay ranging from 4 to 6 weeks, as was the case in the D.C. area last summer, could provide incentives for consumers to go to unauthorized VW dealers (who often make out as if they are authorized) blandishing ads that tout "Fresh VW shipments from overseas." At present the six-week old Atlantic and Gulf coast dock strike has made the delivery period much longer and thereby opened up a greater opportunity for used VW vendors to peddle their in-stock vehicles as new. After the sale was consummated, the defrauded motorists would experience breakdowns and "fast" wearing out of parts. FTC investigators noted that the usage of the vehicles in Europe before being sold to the U.S. could be ascertained by examining the engine manifold, fender wells, tires, brake and clutch pedals and floor mats. But a buyer not alert to his being defrauded would have no occasion to observe these signs, especially in view of the expert cosmetic job done on the cars in Hamburg.

It is pertinent here to note that even franchised dealers are not reluctant to re-title vehicles—that is to call a vehicle a 1969 model when it was actually produced in the 1968 model year as defined by the manufacturer. This is done to sell any oversupply of the past model year. The National Highway Safety Bureau has information that it has not disclosed which persuades Bureau personnel that it has been and is extremely common practice, particularly on the part of importers, to transform the papers on unsold vehicles so that they appear as the new model year's offering. It is the rare motorist who checks serial numbers and determines the period of manufacture. (Neither the National Highway Safety Bureau nor the Federal Trade Commission has done anything about this deception.)

Notwithstanding abundant evidence concerning the used-as-new VW sales practices, the upper staff closed out the investigation. The Commissioners who reviewed the matter were not given the complete files but instead relied on the upper staff's interpretation. The VW fraud continues to the present day with more evidence coming to the FTC and no evidence that the same personnel who closed the inquiry out in 1964 are about to change their mind. The reasons, such as they were, for closing out the inquiry had nothing to do with the widespread nature of the practice. One dealer moved his operations to the West Coast which gave the upper staff the flimsy foundation for closing out a lengthy investigation covering many dealers. The insistent staff recommendation to have the Commission move under Section 5 of the Federal Trade Commission Act and to request Justice Department to start legal action under the Mail Fraud Act were ignored without adequate explanation. Even more inexcusably, the upper staff declined to advise the Commissioners that the public had a right to know of this practice in the form of disclosure of these fraudulent acts. Although dozens of witnesses stood ready to testify regarding their experiences in being sold used VWs as new VWs and had given statements to FTC investigators, and although complaints are still coming to the Commission, the upper staff remains inexplicably adamant about not initiating disclosure, legal action or allocation of greater manpower commensurate with the safety and economic significance of this deceptive practice. Secrecy and enigmas surround this entire episode. It is time that they be cleared up. Inasmuch as the Commission over the years has proven itself incapable of self-correction, self-adjustment and a vigorous pro-consumer posture, your Committee may well see fit to inquire more deeply into this matter.

The Commission has also had some indication that imported vehicles are being sold in this country without having met the federal safety standards. Perhaps they will disclose this information to the Committee.

Thank you for your consideration,

Sincerely yours,
(s) Ralph Nader

## HOW NEW IS YOUR "BEETLE"? *

*By Robert F. Wright*

Seldom is the automobile buyer faced with such bewildering problems as when he shops for a Volkswagen.

An *Action Line* investigation, prompted by numerous complaints, found that hundreds of Washington-Baltimore area residents every year may be bilked out of as much as several hundred dollars each by some dealers.

The national figure may be as high as 20,000 because, while the mid-Atlantic area is a hotbed of problems uncovered by *Action Line,* the situation exists from coast to coast.

The bilkings are centered on Volkswagen's popular "beetle" model only and take many forms, but all add up to the buyer getting something less than that for which he paid.

The problem lies with the VW market situation: The beetle is in such great demand that prospective new-car buyers must wait six to eight weeks to get delivery through authorized dealers—those holding franchises from Volkswagen of America.

Many such purchasers, unwilling to wait, choose to deal instead with unauthorized or "gray-market" dealers who buy their cars from European agents and promise delivery in two weeks or less.

When patronizing an unscrupulous dealer, the buyer may find himself shortchanged in one or more ways.

—He may find himself with a European delivery model with a 15 percent smaller engine, a six-volt electrical system, no smog-control equipment and no replacement parts when major high-mileage service is needed.

—He may find that his warranty is worthless or not what the salesman implied.

—He may find that the Internal Revenue Service wants him to pay excise tax on a car he bought months before.

—Worst of all, he may find that what he thought was either a year-old vehicle with a new-car title or a low-mileage used car is actually an ex-rental car with 15,000 or more miles.

Many of the gray-market cars sold here were built for European use and don't carry the same equipment as American models.

Many of these European models are equipped with en-

* Reprinted from the Washington *Star,* February 16, 1969. Copyright 1969, The Washington Star, reprinted by permission.

gines of 1300-cc. cylinder displacement, 200 cc. less than American delivery models.

It may not sound like much, but in a small car the 15 percent increase changes the auto from one with marginal excess power to one happier in rush-hour and freeway traffic.

It should also mean shorter engine life because the larger engine is strained less to produce the same performance as the smaller one.

A 1300 model was sold in this country by VW several years ago but has since been discontinued and the result may be a parts shortage when the gray-market cars begin to wear out long after the legitimate American model 1300s are dead and gone.

Warranties also cause problems.

One salesman for a gray-market dealer told an *Action Line* investigator: "We only offer a six-month, 6,000-mile warranty, but any authorized VW dealer may extend that to 24 months-24,000 miles."

He was right, but only if the car in question happens to be an American delivery model (the factory offers only a six-month-6,000-mile warranty on European models) and the authorized dealer is willing to give you something for free when you have already deprived him of the car's sale, a major source of profit.

One unauthorized dealer offers his own 24-month-24,000-mile warranty, but it is not factory-backed and is good only in the dealer's own repair shop. Others offer the European warranty, but the expertise of mechanics may be questioned.

One of the gray-market dealer techniques is to import a car in the buyer's name. The buyer, who has already paid the standard gray-market premium price about $50 higher than the authorized dealer price, thinks nothing of the legalities of the importation.

Four to eight months later, the buyer may find that he is being billed by the IRS for up to $140 in excise tax because he is listed with the Customs Bureau as the importer of record.

The gray marketeer, meanwhile, is $140 richer because authorized dealers and some unauthorized dealers import cars in their own names and pay the tax.

Many gray-market buyers think they're getting good deals when they buy last year's models, some with new-car titles and some with used-car titles but very low mileage.

The deals may not be so good.

There are operating in Europe companies that specialize in "rebuilding" late-model Volkswagens.

These firms, according to one unauthorized dealer, may go so far as to strip the car of all trim and running gear, dip it in a paint vat and reassemble it. The result is a car that almost looks like new.

"What difference does it make if a car is rebuilt?" a dealer asked *Action Line*. "It's the way a car looks that matters; that's what sells cars."

He would be right if he could provide evidence that the rebuilding firms took as great care in refurbishing chassis and engine as they do in making the car look new.

But the buyer shouldn't expect too much more than cosmetic rebuilding because the gray marketeers pay only $975 for the year-old cars they retail for $1,700.

Because the odometers of rebuilt cars have been converted from kilometers to miles and often record between 10 and 20 miles, the buyer can't be certain of actual use.

"We don't know how many miles are on the car," one salesman told an *Action Line* investigator looking at a 1968 with 15 miles on the odometer. "It may be 15 or 150 miles."

The salesman was right. He might also have been right if he had said the car could have traveled 1,500 or 15,000 miles because many of the "rebuilt" cars formerly belonged to European car rental firms.

A spokesman for one such rental firm said it was company policy to sell cars after nine months when they have averaged about 20,000 miles.

Because the "rebuilding" of VWs is apparently only superficial, there may be minor clues left of a car's actual age for which the buyer may watch.

The paint on headlight and windshield-wiper switches may show wear, brake and clutch pedals may be worn lopsidedly, horn buttons bearing the VW castle emblem may show minor internal cracking through their clear plastic, paint on road wheel edges may be badly chipped, mufflers may be rusty and heat-aged, and chrome door handles may have varying degrees of pitting.

These items are only superficial and should potential buyers begin to shy away from cars with these obvious signs, rebuilders and gray marketeers can easily replace them. It would only skim off some of the profits.

Non-franchise-holding dealers aren't the only ones selling "rebuilt" cars; Customs Bureau records show that some of the largest authorized VW dealers have occasionally imported some.

Buyers of 1969 models from some unauthorized dealers are also confronted with an assortment of hybrid cars.

While American delivery '69s have padded dashes, "highriser" seatbacks with built-in headrests and smog-control equipment, European models may have all, some or none of these.

A small sticker on the left-side door jamb, indicating that the car meets all federal safety requirements may be worthless: *Action Line* found some similar to, but not exactly like, those stickers applied by the VW factory.

Buyers of '69s may also have a difficult time telling which engine is in a car because some engine compartment lids are marked outside with "Volkswagen," some with "1500" and some with "1300."

The numeral markings should indicate engine size, but an industrious gray marketeer could switch them. Those marked "Volkswagen" may have either engine.

Sometimes, engine crankcases behind a generator belt pully or air-cooling fan shrouds bear an ink-stamped "1.3" or "1.5," but again a dealer could easily remove a "1.3" and replace it with a "1.5" stamp.

Of concern to the general public is the estimate of one Department of Health, Education and Welfare spokesman that 90 percent of the gray-market cars—a figure not in conflict with *Action Line*'s finding—lack smog-control devices.

This would mean that nearly 2 million pounds of carbon monoxide and 400,000 pounds of hydrocarbons are added to the area's atmosphere each year that wouldn't be added if the gray-market cars had controlled engines.

The auto buyer has little protection from a gray marketeer who happens to be dishonest, as auto industry critic Ralph Nader brought to the public's attention last week in a letter to Sen. Warren G. Magnuson, D-Wash., chairman of the Senate Commerce Committee.

The Washington Better Business Bureau, queried by *Action Line* about gray-marketeer problems, gave almost identical reports about a much-complained-about dealer and a dealer never complained about.

The Federal Government has been criticized in the press recently for its failure to probe the problem and provide consumer protection, but *Action Line* had found weeks before that this wasn't the case.

While little action has been taken, investigations are underway by the Federal Trade Commission, HEW, the Department of Transportation, the Customs Bureau, and the Internal Revenue Service.

Volkswagen of America was also chided for its failure to warn the public of pitfalls and a VWoA spokesman responded that the firm feared charges of restraint of trade.

"Legal opinions vary," a government attorney told *Ac-*

*tion Line,* "and if I were a conservative businessman, I might take the same stand."

He cited sections 1 and 2 of the Sherman Anti-Trust Act and said VWoA warnings "might be deemed a conspiracy between VWoA and the franchised VW dealers."

Until governmental investigations are concluded, the consumer can only proceed with caution.

United States Senate
Committee on Commerce
Washington, D.C. 20510

February 24, 1969

Dr. Robert Brenner
Acting Director
National Highway Safety Bureau
Department of Transportation
Washington, D.C.

Dear Dr. Brenner:

On February 7, Mr. Ralph Nader sent me a letter indicating that a large number of used Volkswagens are being imported into the United States and sold here as new automobiles. The Commerce Committee has announced that it intends to look into this problem later this year when it holds hearings on the safety characteristics of small cars. If you have gathered any information on this practice through the implementation of the Traffic Safety Law which would aid us in our inquiry, I would appreciate it if you would forward it to me.

I have also learned that several non-franchised Volkswagen importers have been purchasing new Volkswagens from distributors in Europe and importing them into the United States. Apparently they take these cars, which were originally manufactured for sale in the European market, and have "3 or 4 men work them over" prior to their exportation in order to bring them into compliance with the U.S. safety standards. I would appreciate receiving your opinion on whether such a small operation could successfully do this, or whether, in the case of Volkswagens, some basic structural or equipment changes (such as a different braking system), which would be beyond the capacity of a small garage to readily perform, would be required. In addition, should you have any other information indicating that vehicles which might not comply with the safety standards are being imported into the U.S., I would like to receive it.

Incidentally, I was pleased to learn that the Bureau plans to launch a study of Volkswagen crashworthiness on March 1. I hope that this testing will proceed with all dispatch and that you will have some preliminary test results, and possibly even a movie, available by early April.

I look forward to hearing from you.

Sincerely yours,
(s) Warren G. Magnuson
Chairman

Honorable Warren G. Magnuson
Chairman
Senate Commerce Committee
United States Senate
Washington, D.C. 20510

Dear Mr. Chairman:

This is in further reply to your letter of February 24, 1969, in which you inquired about certain practices of nonfranchised Volkswagen importers: (1) importation of used vehicles into the United States for resale as "new" vehicles, and (2) importation of new vehicles not manufactured for the American market but modified prior to shipment to a state of ostensible conformity with the Federal motor vehicle safety standards.

Section 108(a)(1) of the National Traffic and Motor Vehicle Safety Act of 1966 (15 USC 1397 (a) (1)) provides in part that "No person shall . . . import into the United States, any motor vehicle or item of motor vehicle equipment manufactured on or after the date any applicable Federal motor vehicle safety standard takes effect under this title unless it is in conformity with [any applicable Federal] . . . standard." Section 108(b)(1) does not excuse imported used vehicles from this requirement. Thus, all motor vehicles manufactured on or after January 1, 1968, whether new or used, must conform at the time of importation to standards applicable at the time of manufacture.

The ready market for Volkswagen vehicles has resulted in certain dealer activities outside the franchised distributor-dealer organization. These nonfranchised dealers operate in two principal fashions:

1. By importing both new and used vehicles in their own names, which may not conform to the applicable safety standards, using the exception permitted by 19 CFR §12.80(b)(2)(iii) and (c), the regulations governing importation of motor vehicles subject to the Act. This allows the posting of a bond to assure that a nonconforming vehicle will be brought into conformance within 90 days.
2. By refitting prior to importation primarily used, but possibly also new, vehicles manufactured for foreign markets to bring them into ostensible conformance with the American safety standards.

With reference to the first, in some instances a nonfranchised dealer acts under a power of attorney from a potential customer, with the individual's name appearing as the importer of record. Where a vehicle is imported under §12.80(b)(2)(iii) and (c), it is the responsibility of the individual who granted the power of attorney (or for that matter any importer or consignee of record) to have the necessary modifications made and to submit the compliance statement required by §12.80(c) to Customs officials at the port of entry. All importation and all compliance statements concerning the safety standards are forwarded to the National Highway Safety Bureau for evaluation. The statement also identifies the manufacturer, contractor, or other person who has brought the vehicle into conformity with applicable standards and describes the nature and extent of the work performed. Customs is currently carrying out three redelivery actions as a result of importers' failure to make proper response within the 90 days allowed by §12.80(c). The policing of these cases by both the Customs Bureau and the National Highway Safety Bureau, however, is very difficult because of our small staff, the geographical spread of individual purchasers and inability to determine conformance with certain of the standards without conducting actual tests.

At least 81 nonfranchised dealers, including eight who act principally as wholesalers, are known either to contract with foreign refitting operators to bring foreign versions into ostensible conformance with the United States requirements or to purchase refitted vehicles from the operators. This work is done mostly on used vehicles. After contacts with eight of the nonfranchised operators or their representatives and visual inspections of approximately 400 vehicles by Bureau compliance personnel at the ports of Baltimore, Houston, Los Angeles, New York, Norfolk, and Jacksonville, it is our impression that Volkswagen vehicles now arriving in the United States compare favorably with the American import versions manufactured by Volkswagen, AG. The refitters appear to have a source of genuine Volkswagen parts and reasonably competent mechanics. A great majority of these vehicles are processed by a few large converters in Europe such as:

Carl Tiedman—Hamburg, Germany
Horst Kruger—Hamburg, Germany
Hofcar—Minden, Netherlands
Jan de Ruiter—Veenendaal, Netherlands

Visual inspections, however, can only uncover the readily apparent violations of the Federal safety standards. A more detailed determination would require laboratory and other complex tests, funds for which are severely limited. None have been conducted to date on refitted vehicles manufactured originally for foreign markets.

Vehicles refitted prior to importation are admitted under

the provisions of §12.80(b)(c)(ii), which requires the submission of a certificate by the manufacturer, contractor, or other person who has brought the vehicle into conformance and describes the nature and extent of the work performed. The converters are furnishing such certificates for use by the importers. It is extremely doubtful if these converters could produce test data and records to support their statements. We are looking into ways and means to obtain such information.

I am enclosing a copy of the certification regulations (49 CFR Part 367) which require that the motor vehicle safety standard certification plate for all vehicles manufactured on or after September 1, 1969, include the month and year of manufacture. This identification should serve as a deterrent to the sale of used vehicles as "new" vehicles.

The representation and sale of used vehicles as "new" or previously unowned may be a deceptive practice and within the regulatory province of the Federal Trade Commission. I am forwarding your letter to Mr. Paul Rand Dixon, Chairman, Federal Trade Commission, asking him to send you his comments on this issue.

In reference to the Volkswagen crashworthiness study, you are no doubt aware that a movie of these tests was shown before the Senate Commerce Committee on April 15, 1969.

Sincerely,
(s) Robert Brenner
Acting Director

Federal Trade Commission Press Release, August 12, 1971

USED VOLKSWAGEN DEALER IN
D.C. AREA CITED IN FTC ORDER

The Federal Trade Commission today announced provisional acceptance of a consent order prohibiting German Auto Agency, 3000 N. 10th St., Arlington, Va., from using deceptive sales and credit practices.

The complaint charges that the firm:

- Misrepresented that it is an authorized Volkswagen dealer which has in stock and sells new and unused Volkswagens.
- Did not inform purchasers that their Volkswagens had been manufactured specifically for sale in a foreign market and had different specifications than new Volkswagens of the same year manufactured specifically for and sold by authorized dealers in the United States. (These differences, which are not readily apparent to the public and would be recognized only by trained and experienced persons, affected the cars' performance, the purchasers' convenience and the cost and time for repairs.)
- Did not inform customers that its warranties are not identical to those issued by authorized Volkswagen dealers, and that any work under them is to be performed only at its shop.
- Violated the Truth in Lending Act by not supplying customers with copies of their retail installment contracts, by making inaccurate credit disclosures, and by misrepresenting in advertising the amount of down payment it would accept.

The agreed-to order also names, individually, George Sprague and Ray Culbertson.

The complaint and consent order will remain on the public record from August 12, 1971 to September 10, 1971. Comments from the public received during this period will become part of the public record. The FTC may withdraw its acceptance of the agreement after further consideration.

The agreement is for settlement purposes only and does not constitute an admission by respondents that they have violated the law.

CONSENT ORDER
(File No. 702 3199)

# APPENDIX V:
## VOLKSWAGEN FAILURES IN TESTS FOR COMPLIANCE WITH FEDERAL MOTOR VEHICLE SAFETY STANDARDS

| | *Safety Standard* | *Model* | *Compliance Test Failure* | *Tested by* | *Report Date* | *Investigation* | *Status* |
|---|---|---|---|---|---|---|---|
| 1 | #103 Windshield defrosting | 1969 Sedan | Failed to clear windshield at 1500 rpm engine speed. Manufacturer is permitted two alternative test speeds —passed at 25 mph. (PB-189854) | Dayton Brown | 3/70 | In test by VW, 3.5% of critical area of windshield cleared in 20 min of operation at 1500 rpm. Adequate performance at 25 mph. (CIR-132) | No action; closed 2/2/70 |
| 2 | #108 Lamps and reflectors | 1970 Sedan | Turn signal reflector not adequately bright at several points. (HS-610510) | Industrial Testing | 10/70 | Failure not judged significant. Test procedures alleged to be too arbitrary. (CIR-316) | No action; closed 8/25/71 |
| 3 | #209 Seat belt assembly | 1969 models | Belt retained only 71% of its strength after abrasion; needed 15 pounds to adjust belt. (no number) | Dayton Brown | 1/70 | VW's own tests showed compliance. (CIR-152) | No action; closed 10/30/70 |

**Note: Numbers in parentheses refer to catalogue number at the Technical Reference Room, National Highway Traffic Safety Administration, Department of Transportation.**

Appendix V: *Continued*

| | *Safety Standard* | *Model* | *Compliance Test Failure* | *Tested by* | *Report Date* | *Investigation* | *Status* |
|---|---|---|---|---|---|---|---|
| 4 | #209 | 1969 models | Retractor failed to operate after 1500 cycles; washer rusted. (HS-610682) | Detroit Testing Lab. | 12/70 | Retractor subjected to corrosion test before endurance test. Procedure has since changed. Failure not significant, according to NHTSA. (CIR-332) | No action; closed 5/26/71 |
| 5 | #209 | 1971 models | Required excessive effort to adjust belt. (HS-611194) | Detroit Testing Lab. | 3/71 | Investigation not yet begun, as of 9/1/71. | |
| 6 | #209 | 1971 models | Required excessive effort to adjust belt. (HS-611195) | Detroit Testing | 3/71 | Investigation not yet begun, as of 9/1/71. | |
| 7 | #209 | 1971 models | Excessive effort to adjust; retractor failed. (HS-611512) | Detroit Testing | 7/71 | Investigation not begun as of 9/1/71. | |

| | | | | | | | |
|---|---|---|---|---|---|---|---|
| 8 | #209 | 1971 models | Adjustment effort, retractor. (HS-611513) | Detroit Testing | 7/71 | Investigation not begun as of 9/1/71. | |
| 9 | #209 | 1971 models | Required excessive effort to adjust. (HS-611299) | Dayton Brown | 5/71 | Investigation not begun as of 9/1/71. | |
| 10 | #209 | 1971 models | Assembly corroded. (HS-611298) | Dayton Brown | 5/71 | Investigation not begun as of 9/1/71. | |
| 11 | #209 | 1971 models | Belt failed to withstand specified load. (HS-611340) | Dayton Brown | 5/71 | Investigation not begun as of 9/1/71. | |
| 12 | #210 Seat belt anchorages | 1969 Sedan | Driver's shoulder harness pulled out of door pillar under 2712 pounds of stress. (PB-188689) | Dayton Brown | 1/70 | Investigation file not made public as of 9/1/71. (CIR-151) | Closed 3/15/71 No action. |
| 13 | #301 Fuel system integrity | 1968 Fast-back | Barrier impact at 32.31 mph caused fuel lines from tank to shear; excessive fuel leakage. (PB-187497) | Digitek Corp. | 7/69 | Fuel lines not covered by standard; car exceeded maximum 30 mph. Model in compliance. (CIR-024) | Closed 12/18/69 (see attached letter) |
| 14 | #301 | 1969 Sedan | Barrier impact caused corner of jack mount to puncture tank; excessive leakage. (PB-188180) | Digitek Corp. | 5/70 | Model found not in compliance; VW modified design on 1970 models. (CIR-153) | Closed 5/18/70 (see letters) |

U.S. Department of Transportation
National Highway Safety Bureau
Washington, D.C. 20591

In Reply Refer to:
CIR-153.1

May 4, 1970

REGISTERED MAIL—RETURN RECEIPT REQUESTED

Mr. G. Storbeck
Product Planning Manager
Volkswagen of America, Inc.
Englewood Cliffs, New Jersey 07632

Dear Mr. Storbeck:

The National Highway Safety Bureau has reviewed Volkswagen's response to our CIR-153, regarding possible noncompliance to Federal Motor Vehicle Safety Standard No. 301. These data have been evaluated in conjunction with the results obtained from the Bureau's own barrier impact test.

We have concluded that the jack mounting location in the Type I Volkswagen may create a hazardous safety situation in some vehicle collisions. This conclusion is based upon the following considerations:

1. The Type I Volkswagen subjected to a barrier impact test in the Bureau's compliance testing program resulted in fuel tank rupture by the jack mounting bracket and fluid leakage in excess of the allowable limit of Standard No. 301.
2. The Swedish Government Safety Council Report (No. 155, June 1969) notation of two Volkswagen accidents in which the fuel tank was ripped open by the jack and its conclusion that a more suitable placement for that tool should be found.

Since only a few examples of fuel tank rupture by the assembly are presently known, a defect notification campaign is not considered necessary at this time; however, we reserve the right to reopen this aspect of the case if other examples become known to us.

We feel strongly, however, that changes be made to the jack mounting location to preclude the proven capability of the jack mounting bracket to puncture the fuel tank assembly. Accordingly, we ask that appropriate Volkswagen personnel participate in a meeting with the National Highway Safety Bureau for discussion of engineering changes or modifications in Type I Volkswagen automobiles for elimination of this potential safety hazard.

The meeting will be held on May 5, 1970, at 9:30 a.m., in Room 5222A of the Department of Transportation Building, 400 Seventh Street, S. W., Washington, D.C.

Sincerely,
(s) Douglas W. Toms
Director

U.S. Department of Transportation
National Highway Safety Bureau
Washington, D.C. 20591

In Reply Refer to:
CIR-153.2

July 16, 1970

Mr. G. Storbeck
Product Planning Manager
Volkswagen of America, Inc.
Englewood Cliffs, New Jersey 07632

Dear Mr. Storbeck:

Thank you for Volkswagen's participation in the meeting of May 18, 1970, with the National Highway Safety Bureau. Based on the meeting discussions and Volkswagen's plans to relocate the jack assembly storage position, we plan no further action at this time. We reserve the right, however, to reopen this subject if circumstances warrant.

Sincerely,
(s) Francis Armstrong
Director

CIR-024.3

Dec. 18, 1969

Mr. G. Storbeck
Production Planning Manager
Volkswagen of America, Inc.
Englewood Cliffs, New Jersey 07632

Dear Mr. Storbeck:

The National Highway Safety Bureau has evaluated the data and information submitted by Volkswagen of America relating to CIR-024. These data were supplied by correspondence and through meetings between your staff and cognizant representatives from this Bureau. Also evaluated were the results of a testing program initiated by the Bureau to determine if the 1968 Volkswagen Fastback Sedan complied with the minimum requirements of Federal Motor Vehicle Safety Standard No. 301.

As the Bureau's contractor report indicated, the test was conducted at a velocity slightly above the minimum specified by the standard. This higher speed unquestionably resulted in a greater amount of total energy at impact. The Bureau also recognizes that the fuel lines which failed during impact are not presently included in the scope of Standard No. 301.

Based on these evaluations, the Bureau has resolved that the type of fuel line system utilized in 1968 Volkswagen Fastback Sedans represents a marginal safety condition with potential vulnerability to damage and resulting fuel spillage. Such marginal conditions are considered to be inconsistent with the Bureau's overall objective of reducing deaths and injuries resulting from highway accidents.

No further action on this matter is contemplated at this time, but the case shall be reopened if field information, particularly from accident reports, indicates that this type of fuel system is failing or approaching the point of failure in vehicle collisions.

Sincerely,
(s) [for]
Robert Brenner
Acting Director

## APPENDIX VI: VOLKSWAGEN RECALL CAMPAIGNS

A. 1960–1966 *

VOLKSWAGEN OF AMERICA, INC.,
Englewood Cliffs, N.J., May 13, 1966.

Hon ABRAHAM RIBICOFF,
U.S. Senate,
Washington, D.C.

DEAR SENATOR RIBICOFF:

The enclosed information is submitted to you in reply to the letter which you addressed to us on April 21, 1966, in your capacity as chairman of the Subcommitte on Executive Reorganization.

Respectfully yours,
J. Stuart Perkins.

PRODUCT DEFECT NOTIFICATION REPORT—
VOLKSWAGEN OF AMERICA, INC.

Attached is the information requested in Senator Ribicoff's letter to Volkswagen of America, Inc., dated April 21, 1966. The following comments will be helpful in the evaluation of this material: . . .

3. Domestic automobile manufacturers in the United States sell their cars directly to dealers for retailing. Volkswagen of America sells to 14 regional distributor-wholesalers who, in turn, resell to dealers appointed by them. In order to protect the standing of the distributors with their dealers, VWoA ordinarily directs to the distributors all its communications intended for Volkswagen dealers, as is reflected in the attached information. The distributors are under a contractual obligation to transmit all those communications to their dealers and this obligation has been complied with at all times.

4. To provide you with a complete record of our defect campaigns, we have included not only those two recall campaigns in which we called back cars that had been delivered to owners, but also those pre-delivery campaigns in which defect corrections were made by dealers prior to sale to customers. . . .

We are able to conduct such pre-delivery campaigns in most defect cases because of the long supply line between

* Source: *Federal Role in Traffic Safety,* Hearings before the Subcommittee on Executive Reorganization, Committee on Government Operations, United States Senate, December 1966. Appendix, p. 144.

the factories in Germany and the showrooms of the Volkswagen dealers in the United States. In mass production, it is unavoidable that, in relatively rare instances, product defects or failures are discovered after manufacture. The discovery is made either in company tests of sample production cars or in actual use of the cars by customers. In the case of Volkswagen such defects are usually noticed first in Germany, where the cars are under factory tests as well as in the hands of owners long before the vehicles are available for retail sale in the United States.

As stated above, it was necessary to institute recall campaigns after delivery to customers in only *2 instances* in the United States. In an additional 8 pre-delivery campaigns, it was possible to examine and, so far as necessary, to correct all the suspected cars before delivery to retail customers. In the remaining 11 cases, as the report will show, vehicles were examined for defects and corrected either prior to delivery, at our 300-mile free inspection or, in a few cases, during our regular scheduled maintenance services. . . .

On the following pages we have summarized all Volkswagen of America's recall campaigns and all pre-delivery and preventive maintenance campaigns for model years 1960 to 1966 (to date).

(1959–1966)

I. RECALL CAMPAIGNS

*1. Date: November 29, 1961*

Model: Type 1 Convertible and Karmann Ghia Type 3.

Defect: Excessive play which could result in premature wear of the roller and steering worm.

Number of Vehicles: 2,507.

Procedure: We instructed the Distributors with Service Circular of November 29, 1961 to cause the Dealers to recall these vehicles and advised as to the procedure in those cases where customers had moved.

Success of Action: 2,121 verified replacements

*2. Date: November 23, 1962*

Model: Types 1, 2 and 3.

Defect: One of the factory suppliers had used a material for a washer in the stoplight switch which did not comply with specifications. After frequent use of the brakes, washer failure could result in slow leakage of brake fluid.

Number of Vehicles: 127,455.

During the production period involved, switches were supplied by 4 manufacturers. It was therefore necessary to examine the entire output to find the defective switches.

Procedure: With Service Circular No. 85/62 of November 23, 1962, we instructed all Distributors to cause Dealers to inspect all the above vehicles. We continuously checked dealer warranty records against the vehicles involved and continuously instructed the Distributors to cause Dealers to notify owners of outstanding vehicles by mail and by telephone if there was no response to the letter.

Success of Action: Switches replaced on 61,594 vehicles. Warranty claims submitted by Dealers for inspection of an additional 17,210 vehicles. Many Dealers did not submit claims for all inspections performed because of the small amount of reimbursement involved for inspection only. Substantially all vehicles were inspected.

PREDELIVERY CAMPAIGN

*1. Date: December 16, 1959*

Model: Type 2 Station Wagon.

Defect: Reduction gear shafts were overhardened during manufacture. This could result in breakage of the gear shafts.

Number of Vehicles: 1,400 involved, some of which could have had this defect.

Procedure: Most of these vehicles were already checked at the factory. Our Service Field Engineers were instructed by memo of December 16, 1959 to cause the Dealers to inspect every vehicle of that production range prior to delivery to customer.

Succcess of Action: All vehicles were checked prior to delivery to the customers. Defective reduction gear shafts found in 48 cases.

*2. Date: April 6, 1960*

Model: Type 2 Station Wagon.

Defect: Inadequate lubrication of front wheel bearings which could result in premature bearing wear.

Number of Vehicles: 3,180.

Procedure: The Distributors were instructed with Service Circular of April 6, 1960 to cause the Dealers to correct defect in all vehicles of this production range prior to delivery to customers.

Success of Action: Defect corrected on all vehicles prior to delivery to the customers.

*3. Date: January 30, 1963*

Model: Type 2.

Defect: Binding of parking brake cable. In some cases, it could become difficult to release the parking brake.

Number of Vehicles: 232.

Procedure: With Service Circular No. 11/63 of January 30, 1963, we instructed all Distributors to cause the Dealers to inspect all vehicles prior to delivery to customers.

Success of Action: Substantially all vehicles were inspected. Corrective action was necessary in 37 cases.

4. *Date: February 1, 1963*

Model: Type 2 Station Wagon.

Defect: Improper sealing of front wheel bearing. This could cause greasy brake linings and, therefore, reduce efficiency of front brakes.

Number of Vehicles: 141.

Procedure: With letter of February 1, 1963, we instructed the 3 Distributors who received these vehicles to cause the Dealers to replace the oil seals prior to delivery of the vehicles to customers.

Success of Action: All oil seals were replaced prior to delivery of vehicles to customers.

5. *Date: March 18, 1963*

Model: Type 2 Station Wagon.

Defect: Improper fastening of parking brake cable to backing plate which could cause difficulty in releasing parking brake.

Number of Vehicles: 1,250.

Procedure: With letter of March 18, 1963, we instructed all Distributors to cause the Dealers to install positioning clamps prior to delivery of vehicles to customers.

Success of Action: Dealers installed new positioning clamps in 1,041 vehicles prior to delivery to customers.

6. *Date: March 18, 1963*

Model: Type 2 Station Wagon.

Defect: Improper matching of master cylinder prevented adequate tightening of brake-line fitting, resulting in slow leakage of brake fluid.

Procedure: With letter of March 18, 1963, we instructed the 7 Distributors who received these vehicles to cause the Dealers to inspect all vehicles prior to delivery to customers.

Success of Action: All vehicles were checked prior to delivery to customers.

7. *Date: June 22, 1965*

Model: Type 1.

Defect: Inside diameter of connecting hose between master cylinder and brake fluid reservoir too large which could result in slow leakage of brake fluid.

Number of Vehicles: A total of 250 of these connecting hoses were installed in one assembly plant producing cars for world distribution. Volkswagen of America imported

3,914 vehicles from that production period. All had to be examined to identify the units with this defect.

Procedure: With Service Circular No. T–63/65 of June 22, 1965, we instructed the Distributors to cause the Dealers to check all vehicles prior to delivery to customers.

Success of Action: All vehicles were checked prior to delivery to customers. Replacements performed in 31 cases.

*8. Date: September 3, 1965*

Model: Type 1.

Defect: Improper adjustment of turn-signal switch. Excessive clearance could prevent automatic self-cancelling.

Number of Vehicles: 31,480.

Procedure: All Distributors were instructed with Service Circular No. T–92/65 of September 3, 1965 to cause the Dealers to check these vehicles prior to delivery to customers.

Success of Action: All vehicles checked prior to delivery to customers.

*9. Date: September 26, 1965*

Model: Type 1.

Defect: The float of the sender unit could rest on the enlarged depression on the left side of the tank. As a result, the fuel gauge is inoperative.

Number of Vehicles: 28,291.

Of these vehicles, a very small number was equipped with a type of tank on which this malfunction occurred.

Procedure: Our Distributors were instructed with Technical Service Information, issued by Volkswagenwerk A.G. on September 26, 1965, to cause the Dealers to remove the sender unit and modify it as described in Workshop Bulletin K 23.

Success of Action: Corrective action was necessary on 469 vehicles. This malfunction becomes apparent right after the vehicle is put into operation. Therefore, we are convinced that all vehicles with this defect have been taken care of.

### III. PREVENTIVE MAINTENANCE CAMPAIGN

*1. Date: May 9, 1962*

Model: Type 3.

Defect: Incorrect mounting of bracket for front brake hose which could result in tire touching the hose in extreme turns.

Number of Vehicles: No information available as to the number in the United States as this vehicle was not imported by Volkswagen of America.

Procedure: In view of the possibility that a small number

of these vehicles might have found their way into the United States, Volkswagen of America gave instructions to all Distributors with Service Circular No. 34/62 of May 9, 1962 to correct these vehicles during maintenance inspection.

Success of Action: 9 vehicles modified at dealerships.

2. *Date: March 16, 1964*

Model: Type 2 Station Wagon.

Defect: Inadequate lubrication, sealing and possible incorrect adjustment of front wheel bearings that could result in premature bearing wear.

Number of Vehicles: 45,646.

Procedure: With Service Circular No. 31/64 of March 16, 1964 we instructed all Distributors to cause the Dealers to examine the front wheel bearings of these vehicles during the next maintenance service.

Success of Action: Vehicles were inspected during regular maintenance services. Corrective action was necessary on 17,649 vehicles.

3. *Date: October 20, 1965*

Model: Types 1 and 3.

Defect: Insufficient clearance in slot of clamping nut could prevent correct adjustment, resulting in premature wear.

Number of Vehicles: 22,545.

Procedure: Our Distributors were instructed with Service Circular No. T–102/65 of October 20, 1965, to cause the Dealers to examine all vehicles for the correct width of the clearance slot and the specified torque.

Success of Action: Vehicles inspected during the prescribed regular maintenance services. So far, it was necessary to replace clamping nuts on 655 vehicles.

4. *Date: November 19, 1965*

Model: Type 2 Station Wagon.

Defect: Incorrect location of positioning clamp for overflow tube could result in deformation of tube.

Number of Vehicles: 914.

Procedure: We instructed all Distributors with Service Circular No. T–107/65 of November 19, 1965 to cause the Dealers to check the position of the overflow tube and to replace the backing plate if the location of the clamp for the overflow tube was incorrect.

Success of Action: Replacements performed so far in 248 cases during preventive maintenance. This campaign is still underway.

5. *Date: March 25, 1966*

Model: Type 3.

Defect: Clutch cable guide tubes are too long, interfering with clutch adjustment.

Number of Vehicles: 1,900.

Procedure: Our Distributors were instructed with Service Circular No. T–22/66 of March 25, 1966, to cause the Dealers to shorten the clutch cable guide tube.

Success of Action: This campaign is underway. No data available on results.

IV. PREDELIVERY AND PREVENTIVE MAINTENANCE CAMPAIGN

*1. Date: August 25, 1965*

Model: Type 1.

Defect: Incorrect tightening of self-locking nuts of ball joints resulting in excessive play between torsion arm and stub axle.

Number of Vehicles: 20,893.

Procedure: We instructed all Distributors with Service Circular No. T–87/65 of August 25, 1965 to cause the Dealers to check these vehicles prior to delivery to customers or during the free 300-mile maintenance service.

Success of Action: Substantially all vehicles checked either prior to delivery to customers or during the free 300-mile maintenance service.

*2. Date: September 13, 1965*

Model: Type 1.

Defect: The air cleaner from one supplier could cause interference with the fast idle cam of the automatic choke resulting in improper engine idle.

Number of Vehicles: 24,625.

Procedure: Our Distributors were instructed with Technical Service Information of September 13, 1965, issued by Volkswagenwerk A.G. to cause the Dealers to perform a minor modification on the air cleaner.

Success of Action: All vehicles were checked and corrective action taken, if necessary, either prior to delivery to customers or during the free 300-mile maintenance service.

*3. Date: September 13, 1965*

Model: Types 1 and 3.

Defect: Fuel supply could be interrupted due to improper operation of diaphragm for the fuel cut-off valve causing engine to stall.

Number of Vehicles: 22,779.

Procedure: Our Distributors were instructed with Service Circular No. T–94/65 of September 13, 1965 to cause the Dealers to modify the diaphragm for the fuel cut-off valve.

Success of Action: Corrective action was necessary on 974 vehicles. We are convinced that all vehicles with this defect were taken care of as faulty valves make operation impossible.

*4. Date: September 16, 1965*

Model: Type 1.

Defect: Improper torque on mounting bolts of front-axle beam which in time could loosen, causing front-axle noises and shimmy.

Number of Vehicles: 24,727.

Procedure: The Distributors were instructed with Service Circular No. T–96/65 of September 16, 1965 to cause the Dealers to check all vehicles for correct torque of the bolts prior to delivery of vehicles to customers or during the free 300-mile maintenance service.

Success of Action: All vehicles were checked prior to delivery to customers or during prescribed free 300-mile maintenance service.

*5. Date: September 28, 1965*

Model: Type 2.

Defect: The left windshield wiper coupling rod could touch the main wiring harness which eventually could lead to a short circuit.

Number of Vehicles: 5,494.

Procedures: Our Distributors were instructed with Service Circular No. T–98/65 of September 28, 1965 to cause the Dealers to check all vehicles for sufficient clearance either prior to the delivery of vehicles to customers or during the free 300-mile maintenance service.

Success of Action: Vehicles involved were either checked prior to delivery to customers or during the free 300-mile maintenance service.

B. 1966–1971 *

| *Identification Number* | *Date of Company Notification* | *Make* | *Model* | *Model Year* | *Brief Description of Defect (Manufacturer's Corrective Action)* | *Number of Vehicles Recalled* |
|---|---|---|---|---|---|---|
| 66–0006 | 10–6–66 | Volkswagen | Type 1 Vehicles (Sedans, Convertibles and Karmann Ghia) | 1967 | Possibility that vehicles may be equipped with a stop plate with insufficient overlap between the cast-on stops of the clutch-brake pedals and the floor-mounted stop plate. This may allow the brake pedal to move to an inconvenient position which, while allowing actuation, may cause a delay in brake application. (Replace the subject stop plates.) | 64,596 |
| 66–0036 | 12–23–66 | Volkswagen | Karmann Ghia Convertible and Coupe | 1966 & 1967 | Possibility that the rubber grommet protecting the starter cable at the point where it passes through the panel separating the engine compartment from the storage area beneath the rear seat may be dislodged. This may allow the insulation on the starter cable to chafe through, resulting in a short circuit. (Reroute the battery-starter cable through a new type rubber cushion.) | 20,394 |
| 67–0015 | 2–3–67 | Volkswagen | Karmann Ghia and Four Seater Convertibles | NR | Possibility that vehicles were transported in such a way that the rear brake lines may have become damaged. Damage to brake lines can cause brake fluid to leak out which would eventually result in a loss of brakes. (Inspect and replace lines as necessary.) | 14 |

* Source: *Motor Vehicle Safety Defect Recall Campaigns,* U.S. Department of Transportation.

| | | | | | | |
|---|---|---|---|---|---|---|
| 67–0081 | 9–20–67 | Volkswagen | Type 2 (Buses) | 1968 | Possibility that the Allenhead bolts on the rear axle universal joints were not properly torqued and were occasionally installed without spring washer. This can lead to the loosening and possible loss of bolts. (Install spring washer and retorque bolts as required.) | 1,051 |
| 67–0082 | 9–18–67 | Volkswagen | Type 1 (Sedans) Including Convertibles and Karmann Ghias | 1968 | Possibility that the harness running between the carburetor and the fan housing is not properly affixed by the sheet metal clamp to the fan housing. In this case, it is possible that the wiring is hanging down. In resting on the accelerator cable, the insulation of the harness and wires can be chafed through and lead to a short circuit. (Inspect, install clamp, and replace wiring as required.) | 14,022 |
| 67–0099 | 10–17–67 | Volkswagen | Type 1–Sedans (Types 11, 14, and 15) | 1968 | Possibility that the rubber seal between ventilation tube and gas tank is not properly seated. As a result, gasoline fumes may enter the vehicle interior. (Inspect and reseat rubber seal as required.) | 18,042 |
| 67–0100 | 10–17–67 | Volkswagen | Type 1–Sedans Including Convertibles and Karmann Ghias | 1968 | Possible cracks in the gasoline tank breather tube, especially where the tube is bent. As a result, gasoline fumes may enter the vehicle interior. (Inspect, check, and replace breather tube as required.) | 24,438 |

| *Identification Number* | *Date of Company Notification* | *Make* | *Model* | *Model Year* | *Brief Description of Defect (Manufacturer's Corrective Action)* | *Number of Vehicles Recalled* |
|---|---|---|---|---|---|---|
| 67–0107 | 11–7–67 | Volkswagen | Type 2–Station Wagons and Trucks | 1968 | Possibility that driver compartment door locks could break at the pawl for the rotary latch. If this occurs, the driver or passenger door in the driver compartment is no longer properly locked. (Inspect and replace door locks as required.) | 1,764 |
| 67–0109 | 11–14–67 | Volkswagen | Type 3–Squareback and Fastback Sedans | 1968 | Possibility that the anti-corrosion material applied to the brake discs to protect them during ocean transport was not mixed to specifications and did not wear off as quickly as intended. With this material on the disc, braking action may be affected. (Inspect, test, and remove the subject coating as required.) | 4,388 |
| 67–0125 | 12–15–67 | Volkswagen | Type 1–Sedans Equipped with Automatic Stickshift | 1968 | (Same as 67–0081 above.) | 4,368 |
| 67–0129 | 12–20–67 | Volkswagen | Type 1–Sedans Equipped with Automatic Stickshift | NR | Possibility that the gearshift lever stop plate was not correctly positioned. If this plate is not installed properly, the reverse gear locking device becomes ineffective. Due to this, an inadvertent shift into reverse is possible. (Reposition and adjust the gearshift lever stop plate as required.) | 5,143 |

| | | | | | | |
|---|---|---|---|---|---|---|
| 68–0001 | 1–2–68 | Volkswagen | Type I | 1968 | Fastening bolt of an access hole cover for gear-shift rod may protrude into the spare tire compartment and rub tire damaging side wall. (Correct by replacement with a new type cover.) | 29,022 |
| 68–0002 | 1–9–68 | Volkswagen | Type 2–Station Wagons and Trucks | 1968 | Possibility left and right rear brake lines could be chafed through if the space between brake lines and outer rubber boots for universal joints is not large enough. (Correct by replacing outer dust sleeves if required.) | 14,843 |
| 68–0048 | 5–1–68 | Volkswagen | Beetle 4-Seat Conv. Karmann Ghia | 1968 | Possibility wheel bolts were not correctly torqued and wheels were not correctly centered. If vehicle is operated under such conditions and especially if the hand brake has not been fully released, the wheel bolts may loosen. (Correct by inspection of wheel and wheel bolts and properly centering wheels and torquing bolts.) | 87,860 |
| 68–0070 | 7–10–68 | Volkswagen | Type I, Type II, Type III (Beetle, Conv., Karmann Ghia, Station Wagon, Squareback and Fastback) | 1968 | Possibility that front seat over-the-shoulder/lap safety belts have tendency to gradually loosen their adjustment. If this occurs belts are not kept taut and are not as effective. (Correct by inspection and add a spring device when necessary.) | Approx. 293,000 |
| 68–0103 | 10–17–68 | Volkswagen | Type 2 Bus-like Station Wagon and Trucks | 1969 | Possibility that undersized release buttons installed in windshield washer system. This prevents windshield washers from functioning. (Correct by checking washer system and replacing faulty buttons where necessary.) | 297 |

| *Identification Number* | *Date of Company Notification* | *Make* | *Model* | *Model Year* | *Brief Description of Defect (Manufacturer's Corrective Action)* | *Number of Vehicles Recalled* |
|---|---|---|---|---|---|---|
| 68–0120 | 11–15–68 | Volkswagen | Type 31 and 36 Squareback and Fastback | 1968 & 1969 | Possibility some tires may have incorrect labeling. If condition exists, could result in improper inflation of tires. (Correct by properly labeling where necessary.) | 39,920 |
| 70–0022 | 2–6–70† | Volkswagen | Station Wagon Campmobiles Trucks | 1970 | Possibility that vehicles were transported from one automobile works to another by hooking lines to the tie rods rather than clamping lines to front axle beam. If this condition occurred would cause tie rods to bend and result in front wheel toe-out. (Correct by inspecting and have rods replaced if necessary.) | 11,000 |
| 70–0104 | 8–27–70 | Volkswagen | Type 14 | 1971 | Possibility that material used for mounting bracket for steering column tube was of insufficient thickness. (Correct by replacing steering column tube.) | 41 |
| 70–0109 | 9–1–70 | Volkswagen | Type 1 Convertible | 1970 | Campaign to correct chassis numbers erroneously placed on 1970 vehicles. Chassis involved were numbered with 1971 numbers. | 688 |

† There were no Volkswagen recall campaigns reported in calendar year 1969.

| | | | | | | |
|---|---|---|---|---|---|---|
| 70–0121 | 9–29–70 | Volkswagen | Super Beetle | 1971 | Possibility that brake hose leading from master brake cylinder to reservoir may not be properly installed. (Correct by inspecting the reassembly where necessary.)<br>Possibility that gas tank filler cap does not properly seat in filler neck. (Correct by replacing where necessary.) | 4,900 |
| 70–0142 | 11–5–70 | Volkswagen | Type 1 and 2 | 1971 | Possibility that dash pot mounting bracket may contact fuel hose connecting fuel pump with carburetor. Also, fuel hose may contact sheet metal clamp securing wiring harness to fan housing. If either of these conditions exists, contact will cause hose to chafe through hose wall. (Correct by inspecting and modifying where necessary.) | 6,500 |
| 70–0151 | 12–7–70 | Volkswagen | Type 2 | 1971 | Possibility that brake pressure regulator housing used in production could contain casting flaw. This might cause leakage of brake fluid and possible loss of braking efficiency. (Correct by replacing regulator where necessary.) | 10,000 |
| 71–0005 | 12–28–70 | Volkswagen | Type 1, 3, 4, and Super Beetle | 1971 | Possibility that guide pin in steering column lock may have been damaged in assembly. Also, ignition switch may have manufacturing defect. These conditions could result in difficulty in unlocking steering and starting engine. (Correct by replacing locks and switches where necessary.) | 78,100 |

| *Identification Number* | *Date of Company Notification* | *Make* | *Model* | *Model Year* | *Brief Description of Defect (Manufacturer's Corrective Action)* | *Number of Vehicles Recalled* |
|---|---|---|---|---|---|---|
| | | | | | Possibility that left front hood hinge may rub against wiring harness causing damage to wiring. (Correct by re-routing wiring harness where necessary.) | |
| 71–0029 | 2–16–71 | Volkswagen | Super Beetle Type 1 | 1971 | Possibility that suspension strut mounting on side panel was incorrectly welded during production. If weld fails, could loosen suspension strut and cause loss of steering. (Correct by installing modified panels.) | 6,000 |
| 71–0030 | 2–16–71 | Volkswagen | Super Beetle Type 1 | 1971 | Possibility that slotted nuts on outer left and right tie rod ends connecting steering knuckles were insufficiently torqued. (Correct retorquing nuts to 22 ft. lbs.) | 735 |
| 71–0099 | 6–1–71 | Volkswagen | Type 2 Station Wagon | 1971 | Guide bracket for parking brake may have been improperly manufactured and may bend if excessive force is applied to parking brake lever. This would reduce parking brake system's holding ability. (Correct by replacing bracket.) | 5,000 |

| | | | | | | |
|---|---|---|---|---|---|---|
| 71–0163 | 9–15–71 | Volkswagen | Type 1, 2, 3, and 4 | 1972 | Possibility that brake warning light system may become overloaded when ignition switch is turned off, resulting in damage to transistor. If this happens, brake warning light will remain on even though the braking system is in proper working order. (Correct by installing a diode in brake warning light system.) | 10,000 |
| 71–0164 | 9–14–71 | Volkswagen | Type 2 | 1972 | Possibility that Department of Transportation code numbering was omitted from tires. (Correct by replacing tires.) | 60 |
| 71–0203 | 11–5–71 | Volkswagen | Type 3 Squareback with Auto. Transmission | 1972 | Possibility that the fuel lines may rub against the recirculating systems' exhaust return valves until the walls of the lines chafe open. This condition would permit gasoline to escape, constituting a fire hazard. (Correct by inspecting and properly routing lines and regulators.) | 869 |

# APPENDIX VII:
# THE VOLKSWAGEN EJECTOR SEAT

## *A. FEDERAL STANDARDS FOR SEATS*

1. Proposed Initial Federal Motor Vehicle Safety Standard 207.

*Anchorage of Seats—Passenger Cars*

S1. *Purpose and scope.* This standard establishes requirements for seats, their attachment assemblies, and their installation to prevent failure and dislocation by forces acting on the seat as a result of vehicle impact.

S2. *Application.* This standard applies to passenger cars.

S3. *Requirements.*

S3.1 *General.* Except for folding auxiliary jump seats, and side-facing seats, each occupant seat installation shall withstand the loads specified in S3.1.1 and S3.1.2.

S3.1.1 The following loads shall be applied simultaneously in a forward longitudinal direction—

(a) 30 times the weight of the entire seat;

(b) The total load imposed on the seat by simultaneous application of maximum loads required by Motor Vehicle Safety Standard No. 209 for occupant restraint systems at all designated seat positions, including the loads directly transferred to the seat by the restraint system either from direct attachment or from a change in direction over the seat, and the horizontal friction force resulting from the vertical downward component of the maximum design load of the restraint system and a coefficient of friction of 0.40; and,

(c) The loads imposed by all parts of the 95th percentile adult male occupant restrained by a Type I seat belt in a designated seat position to the rear of the seat being tested when a forward longitudinal deceleration of 30g is applied.

S3.1.2 A load equal to 30 times the weight of the entire seat shall be applied in a rearward longitudinal direction.

S3.2 *Folding and hinged seats.* A hinged or folding seat or seat back shall be equipped with a self-locking, restraining device and a control for releasing the restraining device.

S3.2.1 The release control shall be readily accessible to the occupant of that seat and to the occupant of any seat immediately behind that seat, and shall be constructed to preclude inadventent release, or inertial release when loaded longitudinally or transversely to 30g.

S3.2.2 The restraining device shall not release or fail when the loads specified in S3.1.1 and S3.1.2 are applied.

S3.2.3 After the loads specified in S3.1.1 and S3.1.2 have been applied and removed, the restraining device shall release upon application of a force not greater than 40 pounds to the release control.

S3.3.1 The release control shall be readily accessible to the occupant of that seat and to the occupant of any seat immediately behind that seat, and shall be constructed to preclude inertial release when loaded longitudinally to 20g.

S4. *Demonstration procedures.*

S4.1 Dynamic or static testing techniques may be used.

S4.2 Static testing of seats shall be in accordance with Society of Automotive Engineers Recommended Practice J879a, "Passenger Car Front Seat and Seat Adjuster," November 1963.

S4.3 Distributed loads may be replaced by concentrated loads at the loading centroid.

2. Federal Motor Vehicle Safety Standard 207 as Issued January 1, 1968.

*Anchorage of Seats—Passenger Cars*

S1. *Purpose and scope.* This standard establishes requirements for seats, their attachment assemblies, and their installation to minimize the possibility of failure by forces acting on the seat as a result of vehicle impact.

S2. *Application.* This standard applies to passenger cars.

S3. *Requirements.*

S3.1 *General.* Except for folding auxiliary jump seats and side-facing seats, each occupant seat installation shall withstand the loads specified in S3.1.1, S3.1.2, and S3.1.3.

S3.1.1 The following loads shall be applied simultaneously—

(a) Twenty times the weight of the entire seat in a forward longitudinal direction; and

(b) If the seat belt assembly is directly attached to the seat, the total load imposed on the seat by simultaneous application of maximum loads required by Motor Vehicle Safety Standard No. 209 for all attached seat belt assemblies.

S3.1.2 A load equal to 20 times the weight of the entire seat shall be applied in a rearward longitudinal direction.

S3.3 *Folding and hinged seats.* Except for folding auxiliary seats and seats with backs which are adjustable for occupant comfort only, a hinged or folding seat or seat back shall be equipped with a self-locking, restraining device and a control for releasing the restraining device.

S3.1.3 A load equal to a 3,300 inch pound moment about the "H" point for each occupant position for which the seat is designed shall be applied to the upper cross member in a rearward longitudinal direction.

S3.2 The seat adjusters need not be operable after the application of the loads specified in S3.1.1, S3.1.2, and S3.1.3.

S3.3.2 The restraining device shall not release or fail when a forward longitudinal load equal to 20 times the weight of the entire seat back is applied at the center of gravity of the seat back.

S4. *Demonstration procedures.*

S4.1 Dynamic or static testing techniques may be used.

S4.2 Static testing of seats shall be conducted in accordance with Society of Automotive Engineers Recommended Practice J879, "Passenger Car Front Seat and Seat Adjuster," November 1963, using the values specified in and the procedures applicable to this standard.

S4.3 Distributed loads may be replaced by concentrated loads at the loading centroid.

## *B. ANALYSIS OF LOAD REQUIREMENTS OF FMVSS207*

26. The chart below relates the requirements of Federal Motor Vehicle Safety Standard 207, Severy's findings in "Backrest and Head Restraint Design for Rear-End Collision Protection," and the UCLA student study of *Injury Exposures in a Large–Small Car Collision.*

In the computation of the torque developed on the seat in the UCLA study, an applicable torso weight of 125 lbs. and a 20-inch lever arm for the force were used. The resultant loads on the two front seats in the rear-ended Beetle were then found to be approximately the values given for the driver's seat and the strengthened passenger seat respectively.

Assuming the same torso weight and lever arm length, the equivalent torque of FMVSS 207 can be approximated by using the ratios of the UCLA study. These are the figures given in the table. Thus, an acceleration of only about twice the acceleration of gravity would exceed the requirements of this standard.

Only orders of magnitude should be compared on this

chart. The chart shows that the acceleration of a torso in the Ford was only about half that in the VW when each was impacted by a Ford traveling 30 mph. Also, one can see that, even for the Ford, the requirements of FMVSS 207 would not be met even in a 10-mph crash.

| *Reference* | *Speed of Impacting Car (mph)* | *Peak Acceleration (g)* | | *Torque about Seat Back Pivot (inch-lbs.)* |
|---|---|---|---|---|
| | | *Car Frame* | *Torso* | |
| FMVSS 207 S3.1.3 | Not specified | Not spec. | 1.8 | 4,250* |
| FMVSS 207 S3.1.2 | Not specified | Not spec. | 2.2 | 5,200 |
| UCLA study (Ford into VW) | 30 | 25 | 13–18 | 30,000–42,000 |
| Severy (Ford into Ford collisions) | 10 | 5 | 4–5 | Not calculated in the study. |
| | 20 | 8 | 5–6 | |
| | 30 | 9–12 | 6–9 | |
| | 40 | 19 | 10–18 | |
| | 55 | 19 | 14–33 | |

* While the test specifications of FMVSS 207 S3.1.3 require the application of a 3,300 inch-pound torque about the seating reference point, this is equivalent to 4,250 inch-pound torque about the pivot point of the VW seatback, since this pivot is below the seating reference point.

# APPENDIX VIII:
# FIRES IN VOLKSWAGEN CRASHES *
# BURNS IN AUTOMOBILE ACCIDENTS

Bengt Pontén

*From the Department of Plastic Surgery,
Akademiska Sjukhuset, University of Uppsala, Sweden*

*Abstract.* In a series of 94 Swedish road accidents with cars catching fire, 72 persons sustained burns (mortality 53%). The most violent fire occurred when the fuel tank was damaged. This happened in 80% of those cars with front fuel tank. By comparing 42 fires in front tank cars with 49 in rear tank cars, the following facts could be established: Although front tank cars in Sweden constitute only 20% of all passenger cars, they are responsible for 46% of the fires, 80% of the burns, and 88% of the fatal burns.

Road accidents with cars catching fire are relatively uncommon, but the burns sustained are usually severe and the mortality high. At the Plastic Surgery Department of the University Hospital in Uppsala, we have seen 11 burns caused by fire in 7 passenger cars. Three patients died; three were seriously burned but survived; two escaped with less extensive, but deep, burns; and three with minor burns. Inquiries into the details surrounding these seven accidents showed that in all cases fuel had been ejected and caused violent fires. In five cases the cars causing the fire had the fuel tank in the front, one had the usual rear tank, while one car had extra fuel tanks in the front seat.

The seriousness of these accidents, and the high percentage of front tank cars led to further inquiries as to the frequency of this particular type of accident. Since June 1966, the police have been required to report all fire accidents to the Swedish Board of Traffic Safety, but when this investigation was started, neither the insurance companies nor the traffic authorities in Sweden registered accidents of this particular type separately. There remained, therefore, only one way to collect this information that is, by reference to newspaper reports. Details of the reported accidents thus collected have afterwards been verified with the aid of police, fire brigade and hospital records.

The group has been limited to include only passenger cars which have caught fire in connection with road accidents. Other types of vehicles have been excluded, as well as fires which have arisen spontaneously.

* Source: *Scandinavian Journal of Plastic and Reconstructive Surgery, 1968,* Vol. 2. Reprinted by permission of the author.

*MATERIAL*

This study comprises 94 accidents which occurred in Sweden during a 5-year period (1962–1967). There were 216 occupants of the cars causing the fire. Of these, 61 were killed and 108 injured. In 70 accidents, the cars collided with other vehicles carrying a total of at least 135 occupants (21 killed, 69 injured). The figures in this group, however, are not exact since there have been more than two cars involved in some accidents, and five others involved buses with an unknown number of passengers. In any case, at least 12 accidents have caused secondary fires in other vehicles.

*BURNS*

These 94 accidents have caused 72 burns: 38 died, 23 sustained serious to moderate burns, and 11 escaped with minor burns (Tables I and II). Of these, only 3 were victims of secondary fires, but two of the latter were fatal.

TABLE I

Number of Fire Accidents With and Without Burns

| *Type of car causing the fire* | *No. of accidents* | | |
|---|---|---|---|
| | *With burns (one or more)* | *Without burns* | *Total* |
| RT-cars | 7 | 42 | 49 |
| FT-cars | 30 | 12 | 42 |
| ET-cars | 3 | — | 3 |
| *Total* | 40 | 54 | 94 |

RT, rear tank; FT, front tank; ET, extra tank.

TABLE II

Fire Accidents Classified According to the Location of the Fuel Tanks in the Cars, Types and Numbers of Burns

| *Type of car causing the fire* | *Types and numbers of burns* | | | | |
|---|---|---|---|---|---|
| | *Fatal* | *Serious* | *Moderate* | *Minor* | *Total* |
| RT-cars | 4 | 3 | 2 | 4 | 13 |
| FT-cars | 30 | 7 | 9 | 6 | 52 |
| ET-cars | 4 | 1 | 1 | 1 | 7 |
| *Total* | 38 | 11 | 12 | 11 | 72 |

Abbreviations as in Table I.

*Fatal burns*

Of the 38 killed, 31 were burned to death by flames in, or close to, the car. In some accidents, desperate screams have been heard from the cars by helpless witnesses who were unable to render assistance, due to fire and the danger of explosion. Identification of the deeply charred bodies has sometimes been extremely difficult, and was successful in one case, only with the aid of the victim's dentist. All fires, however, have not been so violent—more than 50 persons have been rescued from the cars with or without injuries.

Several of the occupants with fatal burns have also had other potentially fatal injuries. In a few cases these have been revealed by autopsy. In other cases, autopsy has not been performed, and the cause of death has been registered as *Combustio totalis*. The presence of other fatal, or less serious injuries is, of course, not revealed in these cases. In 6 patients who died in hospital, burns have been the only cause of death.

*Non-fatal burns*

This group comprises 34 burns. Three persons have had fatal injuries and also sustained non-fatal burns. Fourteen passengers suffered other non-fatal injuries besides burns, while 17 persons have had burns only.

Eleven victims of serious burns were left with gross deformities, such as horribly scarred faces and/or amputated fingers and hands. These patients have required prolonged hospitalization and, sometimes, 10–20 surgical procedures.

Twelve persons sustained less serious burns. Most of these required hospitalization and surgery, but the final disability has been of a less serious degree, such as impaired joint mobility and less extensive scars.

Eleven persons sustained minor burns with no resulting disability.

## *CAUSES OF FIRE*

Analysis of the causes of the fires revealed that those accidents in which fuel leakage had occurred had brought about

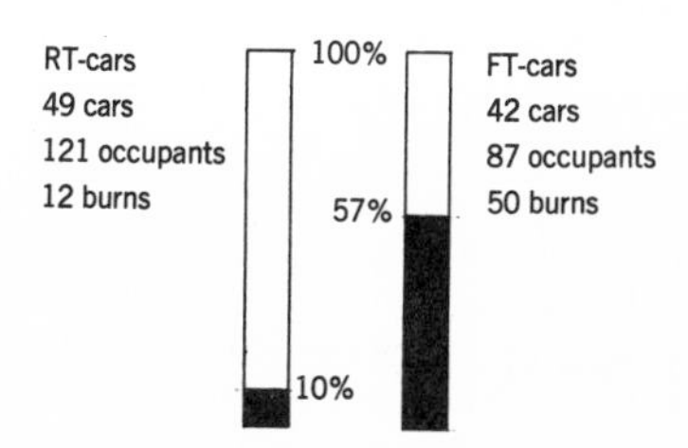


*Fig. 1*. The number and percentage of occupants burned in the cars causing the fire. The victims of secondary fires are not included. FT, front tank; RT, rear tank.

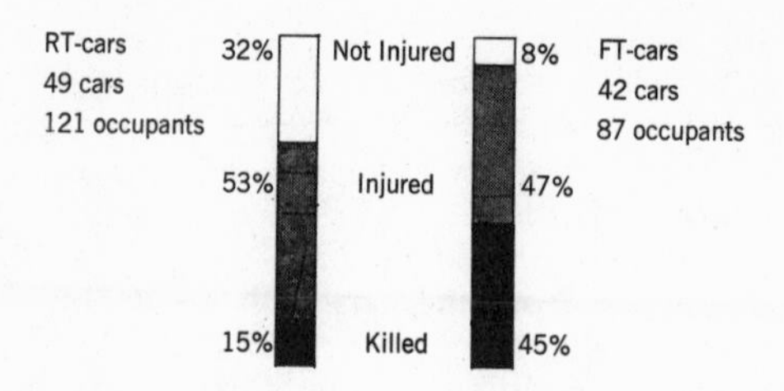


*Fig. 2.* The number and percentage of all injuries (burns included) sustained by occupants of the cars causing the fire.

the most violent fires, and had caused most of the burns, including the most severe burns. In other accidents, the causes have been short circuits, smaller fires in the carburetor, etc. It has not always been possible for the police to determine the cause of fire, however the fuel tank had probably been damaged in about 50% of the accidents.

In 3 accidents, reserve tanks with extra fuel had been kept in the front part of the car. This gave rise to very serious fires. These three accidents alone caused 4 fatal and 3 non-fatal burns. This is, of course, hardly surprising. It is, therefore, strongly recommended that if reserve fuel tanks are considered necessary they be situated in a safe place.

*LOCATION OF THE FUEL TANK*

It has been shown earlier that front impact is the most common type of accident on Swedish roads. A recent study carried out by a Swedish motor car company (Volvo) included more than 28,000 car accidents in Sweden. This study revealed that front impacts constitute more than 35%, and rear impacts 8% of the total. It is, therefore, reasonable to assume that cars with the fuel tank in the front (FT-cars) would be more liable to catch fire than cars with the fuel tank in the rear (RT-cars). This proved to be the case in this study:

1. After excluding the above mentioned reserve tank fires, there remain 91 accidents of which 42 (46%) involved FT-cars (36 Volkswagen, 3 Porsche, 2 BMW 700, 1 Fiat 600) and 49 (54%) involved RT-cars (15 Volvo, 8 Ford, 4 Opel, 4 Renault, 3 Mercedes, 3 Vauxhall, 2 Saab and 1 car each of 10 other different makes). The high proportion of FT-cars is evident since the number of FT-cars in Sweden during this period constituted only 20% of the total. Thus, for instance, the most common passenger car in

Sweden, Volvo, a RT-car, has caused only 15 fires as compared with the next most common car, Volkswagen, a FT-car, with 36 fires.

2. As previously mentioned, the most violent fires arise when the fuel tank is damaged. This has been the case in at least 80% in the FT-group, compared with about 30% in the RT-group. As a result, 30 out of 42 fires in FT-cars have caused one or more burns, compared with only 7 out of 49 in RT-cars (Table I).

3. Although the FT-group is the smaller one, it is responsible for not only a higher number of burns but also the most severe burns. Altogether these cars have caused 52 burns (30 fatal) compared with 13 burns (4 fatal) in the RT-group (Fig. 1).

4. There is also a greater risk of being burned to death in the FT-cars: in this series 23 occupants (3 in RT-cars).

5. Higher figures are found for the FT-cars if other occupant injuries are considered also. Of the 87 persons in these cars 45% were killed. The corresponding figure for 121 persons in RT-cars is 15% (Fig. 2).

*DISCUSSION*

This study is, of course, open to criticism as it is based on newspaper reports, and, therefore, could give a false picture. However, this was the only means of collecting material at the time the study was initiated. It is fully realized that there have probably been other fires which have never been reported in the newspaper, and that there have been others which have been overlooked in the search. Finally, there is always a possibility—although it seems rather remote—that the newspapers might have selectively reported some accidents to the advantage or disadvantage of a particular make of automobile.

This fairly large group of fires should, however, give a reasonably accurate picture of true conditions. Paragraphs 2–5 above are a simple comparison of 42 fires in FT-cars with 49 in RT-cars. Still the incidence of burns is four times as high in the FT-group. Considering the fact that the FT-cars constitute only 20% of Swedish cars, the figures are actually even more striking. In the author's opinion it is highly improbable that a random distribution would be so heavily weighted in favour of one group.

It seems reasonable, therefore, to draw the following conclusions from this series:

1. Road accidents complicated by subsequent fire are relatively uncommon, but they constitute an added danger to the occupants in the form of burn injuries. In this

series of 94 accidents, 72 persons sustained burns (mortality 53%).

2. Front tank cars are more liable to catch fire than rear tank cars.
3. The fires in front tank cars are often very severe since the tank is more easily damaged.
4. Excluding the fires from reserve tanks, it is found that front tank cars are responsible for 80% of the burns and 88% of the fatal burns in these cases.

Recent investigations made in the laboratories of the Swedish Volkswagen representative have shown that a blow striking the fuel tank easily dislodges the tank cap. Fuel is thus ejected from the tank and is readily ignited. A new safety tank cap has now been devised and distributed to all Volkswagen-owners in Sweden.

The fact that the tank cap is so easily dislodged might explain the seriousness of some of the fires, although the risk of damage to the tank itself still remains.

It is fully realized that this group of burns is small compared with the total number of victims in traffic accidents. This does not mean that it can be disregarded. There is, unfortunately, no "push-button-solution" to the problem of traffic accidents. The only logical approach is to analyze in detail the complicated circumstances leading to an accident, and attempt to solve each of the numerous individual problems. With the aid of modern technics it should be comparatively simple to eliminate the risk of fire in today's modern automobile.

# Index